Go for Scie...

Martin Hollins
Peter Horsfall
Janet Major
Mary Whitehouse

Nelson

Thomas Nelson and Sons Ltd
Nelson House Mayfield Road
Walton-on-Thames Surrey
KT12 5PL UK

Thomas Nelson Australia
102 Dodds Street
South Melbourne
Victoria 3205 Australia

Nelson Canada
1120 Birchmount Road
Scarborough Ontario
MIK 5G4 Canada

First published by Thomas Nelson and Sons Ltd 1997

Thomas Nelson, a division of Thomson Learning

ISBN 0-17-438703-2
NPN 9 8 7 6 5 4 3

We are grateful to the following teachers and advisers for their
help in trialling and reviewing *Go For Science*!

Mr John Almond, Amble Middle School, Amble, Morpeth
Ms Ann Brown, Queen's Croft School, Lichfield
Ms Wendy Fairbank, Advisory Teacher Base, Formby
Ms Jane Giffould, Homestead School, Langham, Colchester
Mr Seith Grierson, Monk's Dyke School, Louth
Mrs Margaret Higson, Blue Coat School, Oldham
Dr R.N. Higton, Lord Williams's School, Thame, Oxfordshire
Mr R.E. Hodges, Woolston County High School, Woolston,
Warrington
Mr D. Hollanby, Alsop High School, Liverpool
Mr Mark Levesley, Sussex House School, London
A. McHale, Litherland High School, Sterrix Lane, Liverpool
Mr G. McManus, Hundred of Hoo School, Hoo,
Rochester
Ms Paula Mellors, Castle Vale School, Birmingham
Mr Bryan Miller, Marland Fold School, Oldham
Ms Jane Miller, Springhill High School, Rochdale
Mr A.P. Monaghan, Hardman Fold School, Failsworth,
Manchester
Mr S Morris, Philip Southcote School, Addlestone
Ms Julie O'Malley and Julie Swayle, Southlands School,
Tynemouth, North Shields
Mrs K. Pearn, Rooks Heath High School, South Harrow

Mr Steve Pickersgill, Wycombe High School, High Wycombe
Mr Irwin Pryce, Mount Gilbert Community School, Belfast
Mr Mark Smallwood, Mrs Gillian Sheeran, Mr W.M. Leyland
and Mr. A-J Abbass, Hathershaw Comprehensive School,
Hathershaw, Oldham
Mrs Truman, Plumstead Manor School, London
Mrs D. Wyatt, Moor Park High School, Preston

Readability adviser: Sheila Savage, SENARC, Battledown
Centre, Cheltenham
Safety adviser: CLEAPSS School Science Service, Uxbridge

Acquisitions Editor: Mary Ashby
Development Editor: Mark Lawrence
Editor: Sue Baker
Production: Liz Carr
Concept Design: Michael Fay
Design: Vivienne Gordon
Illustration: Oxford Illustrators
Picture Research: Image Select

CONTENTS

Variety of Life

Sound and Light

Materials and Mixtures

Humans and Health

Forces and Electricity

New Substances

Glossary

Living or not?

Look at this picture.

1 Make a list of five living things you can see.

2 Make a list of five things which are not living.

3 How can you tell if something is living? Write down four ways you can tell.

4 If you were looking for living things in the woods, where would you expect to find them? Write a list of places you would look.

Signs of life

The woodland is the home of many living things.
They look very different from each other.
They have some things in common.

badger

dipper

1 Make a list of all the living things you can
  see in this picture.

2 Make a list of the animals.

3 Make a list of the plants.

4 Write down two ways in which plants are
  different from animals.

5 Write down two ways in which plants and
  animals are similar.

daisy

All living things show these signs of life.

• They feed to get substances to give them energy, to make them grow and to make them healthy.

• They **respire** to get energy from their food. Most living things need oxygen for this.

• They grow using substances in their food. They get bigger and may change in other ways too.

• They move themselves, or parts of themselves. This helps them to survive.

• They sense things that change around them. They react to the changes.

• They **excrete** waste substances which have been made in their bodies.

• Adults **reproduce** to make new living things like themselves. The new ones will take the places of adults that die. This can increase the number of living things.

Looking at animals

Many animals look similar.
If we look closely we can find differences.
There are many different types of animals.

The mice in these pictures all have things in common which make them look alike.

Some important things about them are different.

Animals that are different cannot mate with each other and reproduce.

Each different type of animal is called a **species**.

These mice all belong to the same species. They could all mate with each other and reproduce.

They do not all look exactly the same. The differences between them are called **variations**.

dormouse

wood mouse

field mouse

wild mouse

pet mice

Look at the picture of wild mice.

1 Write down three ways that they look different.

2 Write down two things that they have in common.

Look at the picture of pet mice.

3 Write down two differences you can see between the pet mice.

4 Complete this sentence.
Living things that can reproduce with each other all belong to the same ....

Sorting animals

Scientists sort things into groups or classes. They **classify** them.
This helps people to study living things in an organised way.

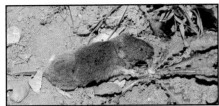

All the animals in these pictures belong to a group of animals called **vertebrates**.

They all have a skeleton inside their bodies. Their bodies have a backbone.

There are five groups of vertebrates – mammals, birds, reptiles, amphibians and fishes.

▲ Mammals have bodies covered with hair. They give birth to live young. They are warm blooded.

▼ All amphibians (*am-fib-ee-ans*) have a smooth, moist skin. They lay eggs in water. The eggs have a case made of jelly. They are cold blooded.

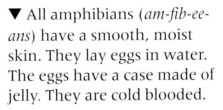

▲ Birds have bodies covered with feathers. They have wings. They lay eggs with a hard shell. They are warm blooded.

▲ Reptiles have bodies covered with a skin made of tough scales. They lay eggs which have a leathery shell. They are cold blooded.

▲ Fish live in water. They have bodies covered in scales. They have fins to help them move. They lay eggs in water. They are cold blooded.

Look at the woodland animals on pages 2 and 3

1 Make a list of four mammals. What do they have in common?

2 Make a list of four birds. What do they have in common?

3 Write down two things a frog and a toad have in common. What group do these animals belong to?

4 Write down two things which are the same in a lizard and a snake. What group do these animals belong to?

Parts of plants

Plants do not move about from place to place.
Green plants make their own food.
The parts of a plant help to keep it alive. Each part is called an organ.

1 The leaves makes food for the plant. They use energy from sunlight to make sugar from carbon dioxide and water. This is called **photosynthesis**.

2 Carbon dioxide gas enters the leaves through tiny holes.

3 Oxygen gas is made in the leaves by photosynthesis when it is light.

4 The roots hold the plant in the soil and draw up water and other things which it needs.

5 The stem carries water up to the leaves and other parts. It also carries food down to the roots.

6 Flowers make seeds, which grow into new plants, Each seed has a store of food in it.

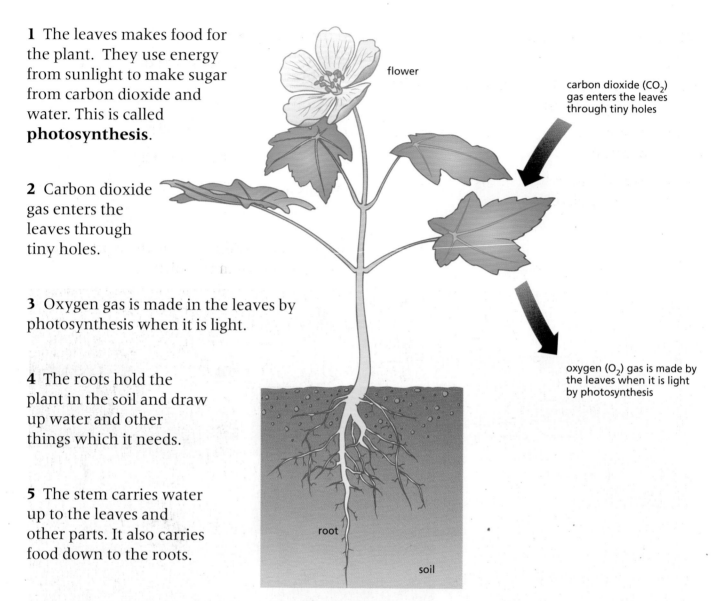

flower

carbon dioxide (CO_2) gas enters the leaves through tiny holes

oxygen (O_2) gas is made by the leaves when it is light by photosynthesis

root

soil

1 Write a list of different types of food you eat which come from plants.
Say which part of the plant you are eating.

2 Make a list of things in the room which came from plants.

3 Write a sentence to say what jobs these parts of a plant do.

| roots | leaves | stem | flower |

Plants are very important for all living things on Earth.

Animals eat parts of plants. Animals use the food made by a plant.

Plants also make oxygen in their leaves by photosynthesis.

Animals and plants need to breathe in oxygen to stay alive.

Humans use plants in many other ways.

All of these things are made from parts of plants –

paper   cooking oil

cotton   some medicines

wood   cardboard

People eat many different parts of plants too. Some are shown in this picture.

Flowers

Many plants make flowers. These contain the reproductive parts of the plant. The flowers often have male and female organs.

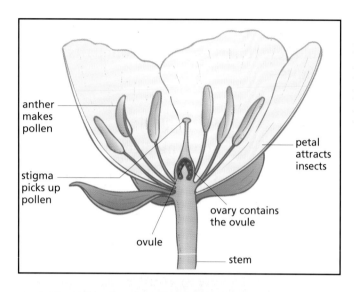

anther makes pollen

stigma picks up pollen

petal attracts insects

ovary contains the ovule

ovule

stem

Coloured flowers attract insects to them. The insect gets food from a flower.

Insects move from flower to flower, collecting food. When they land they also pick up **pollen** from the **anthers**.

The insects carry the yellow grains of pollen from flower to flower.

Some of the pollen lands on the **stigma** of another flower. This pollen grain can join with the **ovule** in the **ovary**. This is called **fertilisation**. A seed is made when a pollen grain joins with an ovule.

1 Make a list of the parts of a flower. Write down what each part does.

2 Make a list of insects which visit flowers.

3 Look at the pictures of the woodland on pages 1, 2 and 3.
Write the names of three plants which have flowers.

4 Make a drawing of the flower in the photograph above. Label its parts.

Looking at seeds

A seed is made when an ovule is fertilised by pollen. The seed contains a young plant. The seed also contains a store of food.
This food is put there by the plant to help the seed grow.

The young plant uses the food store in the seed to help it grow.

Animals like eating seeds because they have a lot of food in them.

Seeds are important foods for many animals in the woodland.

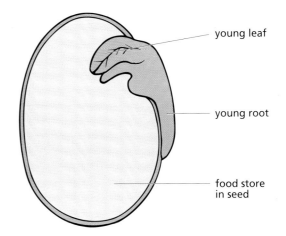

young leaf

young root

food store in seed

People eat seeds too. Peas, beans, rice, and lentils are all seeds.

Farmers plant many crops to grow seeds for us to eat.

Some seeds are used to make other food for us.

Bread is made from flour. Flour comes from wheat seeds.

1 Draw the inside of a seed. Label the young plant. Label the food store.

2 Why do seeds contain a store of food?

3 Name two woodland animals which eat seeds.

4 Make a list of seeds which we eat.

5 Make a list of foods which are made from seeds.

Growing seeds

Seeds grow into young plants.
Seeds and young plants will not survive if the conditions
are not right.

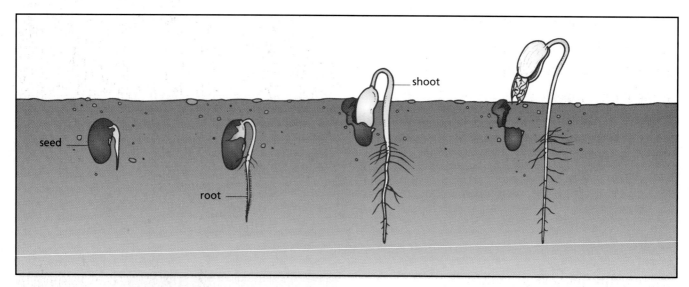

Plants grow in several stages. The first stage of growth is called **germination**.

Not all seeds find the right conditions to germinate.

Some young plants do not live very long.

Plants make a lot of seeds.

Seeds need water and warmth and oxygen to be able to germinate.

Each seed will only grow if it gets the right conditions.

The young plants need light and substances from the soil to make them grow and be healthy.

1 Draw a diagram showing a seed beginning to grow into a plant. Label the parts of the young plant.
2 Make a list of the things a seed must have when it begins to grow.
3 Why do you think plants have to produce lots of seeds?
4 Look at the picture of seedlings trying to grow. Write a list of reasons why seeds may not grow into a healthy plants.

Seeds and survival

Plants keep their seeds inside their fruit until it is ripe. The fruit helps to spread the seeds away from the parent plant. Plants have many ways of scattering them.

Some fruits are scattered by the wind.

They may have wings which help to keep them in the air for a long time.

Some fruits have feathery parts. They can float about in the air.

Some fruits are scattered by animals.

They may have hooks or spikes which catch on to the fur of animals.

Some are sticky to help them stick to animals which carry them away.

These fruits are eaten by animals.

They are sweet and juicy to make them look good to eat.

An animal eats the fruit. The seeds pass through the animal's body and come out of the animal with its droppings.

1 Why do you think seeds need to be scattered away from their parent plant?

2 Choose three of the fruits on this page. Draw each fruit. Write a sentence for each fruit to say how it is spread from the parent plant.

Trees

Trees are plants which can grow very tall. They take many years to reach their full size. When they die they rot away.

Trees are very important to our lives. They make oxygen by photosynthesis. We need oxygen to breathe.

Trees also provide us with many of the things we use every day. Some are shown here.

Many different types of tree grow in the woodland. One way that we can tell them apart is by the shape of their leaves.

oak

ash

chestnut

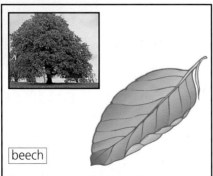

beech

pine

fern

rotting log

moss   woodlice   fungi

Decomposers

When a tree dies, it rots away. Some parts rot quickly. The trunk takes years to rot.

Woodlice and other animals feed on the dead wood.

Fungi grow on rotting wood. Fungi are not plants. They cannot make food by photosynthesis. They get their food from the wood. They reproduce by making spores.

Bacteria are living things which are too small to see without a microscope. They also help to rot the wood. Bacteria using rotting plants as food.

1   Write a list of things which are made from trees.

2   How do trees make oxygen? (See Lesson VL5.)

3   Make a list of all of the living things which feed on the wood of dead trees.

4   Leaves rot away faster than the tree trunk. Why do you think this is?

5   How are fungi different from plants?

Animal homes

Many different animals live in the woodland. Each type of animal needs to find a place to live. Each type needs the right conditions for it to stay alive.

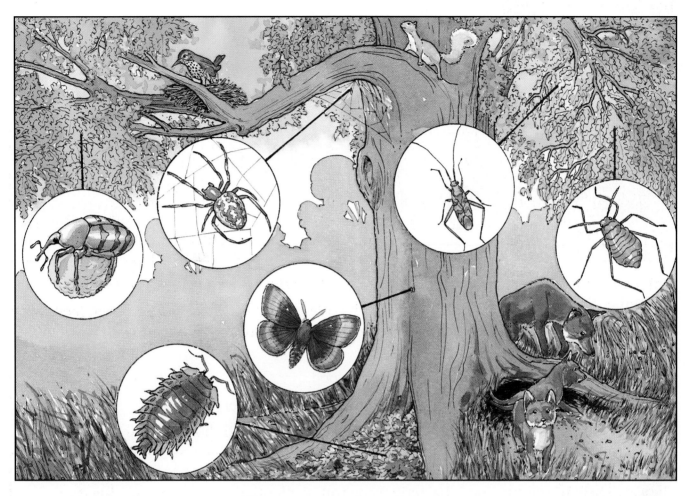

The place where an animal or plant lives is called its **habitat**.

Trees provide many different habitats for animals. The animals need to find shelter from bad weather, and from enemies. They need to be near a supply of food. When a tree is cut down, the lives of many animals will also be affected.

1 What are the things that animals need if they are to stay alive?

2 Make a list of the different animals that might live in a tree.

3 Why would you not expect to find woodlice living at the top of a tree?

4 Why do many people think it is a bad idea to cut down trees?

5 What do the animals in a tree feed on?

Think of two ideas

Finding food

Animals need to find food. Some animals eat plants, some eat other animals. Living things depend on each other for food. A food chain shows this.

Scientists find out what animals eat by watching them feeding.

They may also find out by looking at droppings left by animals.

This owl has fed on a mouse. The bones can be seen in the pellet it produces after feeding.

The mouse is feeding on grass seeds.

We can tell which animal has been feeding by looking closely at what is left.

A food chain diagram is used to show what animals feed on.

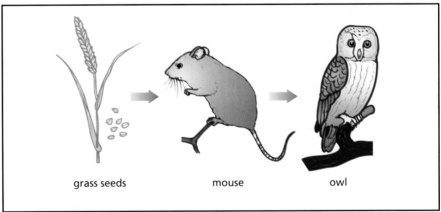

grass seeds   mouse   owl

1 Draw a food chain diagram showing an owl, grass seeds and a mouse.

2 Look at the pictures of aphids. What do aphids eat? What feeds on aphids?

3 Draw a food chain diagram showing leaves, ladybirds and aphids.

The food web

A food web shows how different food chains are linked in nature. Each animal feeds on more than one type of food. Each food may be eaten by more than one animal.

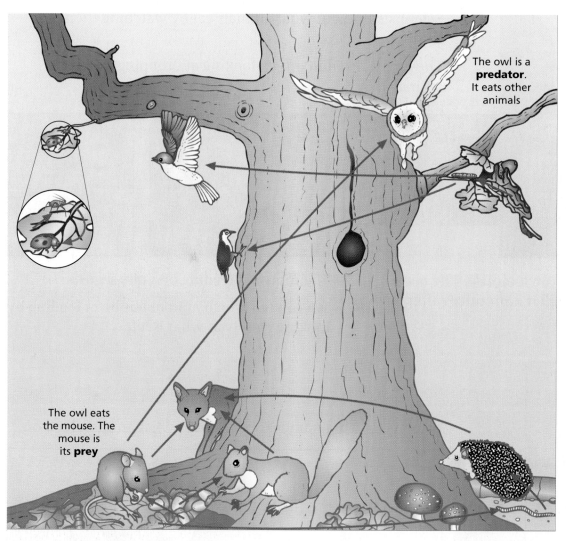

The owl is a **predator**. It eats other animals

The owl eats the mouse. The mouse is its **prey**

Trees are an important source of food in the woodland. Different parts of the oak tree are eaten by different animals.

The owl is a **predator**. It eats other animals. The owl eats the mouse. The mouse is its **prey**.

1 Make a list of all the animals which feed on the oak tree.

2 Make a list of all of the animals which eat mice.

3 What animals does the fox eat?

4 Write a sentence to explain what a predator is.

5 Draw two food chains that you can see in the food web picture.

Woodland birds

Many different types of bird live in woodland. They eat different types of food.

Some birds, such as the eagle, eat small mammals like mice. Others, like the chaffinch, mostly eat the seeds of plants. The thrush catches small insects to eat.

These birds have beaks with different shapes. Each shape is right for a different type of food. The birds' beaks are **adapted** for getting the right food.

1 Draw the beaks of the birds in the pictures.

2 Write down what you think each bird feeds on.

3 Why are pointed beaks best for catching insects?

4 Why are blunt beaks best for picking up seeds?

5 How is the eagle's beak adapted to help it eat meat?

Adapting to change

The weather and the food supply change with the seasons. Living things must find a way to stay alive even when things around them change.

Animals and plants behave differently in each season.

During spring and summer there is a lot of food about. New plants grow. Many animals have their young at this time.

Some birds fly to other countries in the autumn. This is called migration.

During winter it is cold and there is less food. Many animals are less active during winter. Many plants lose their leaves.

1 Write about how the seasons are different from each other.

2 Describe how a tree changes in each season.

3 Describe what mice do in each season.

4 Why do you think some birds fly to other countries during autumn?

Surviving the winter

Winter is the hardest time for living things to stay alive. Woodland plants and animals are adapted to survive in winter conditions.

These plants all have different ways of avoiding the hard winter conditions. Some plants die down so that there are hardly any parts left above the ground. Many kinds of tree lose their leaves in winter. Other trees, like the holly, keep their leaves in winter. They have leaves which are thick and waxy. They are adapted to help them survive.

Many animals build up food stores inside their bodies before winter. They find a safe place to shelter until the weather gets warmer.

1   Why is winter a difficult time of year for living things? Write down two reasons.

2   Write a sentence about what one plant does to survive the winter.

3   Write a sentence about what one animal does to survive the winter.

4   Some birds fly to other countries to avoid the winter. What is this called ?

Sounds all around

There are many **sources** of sound in the world around us.
The source of a sound is the thing it comes from.
We use different words to describe sounds.

Describing sounds

We can describe a sound by its **pitch** and its **loudness**.

Pitch tells us how high or low a sound is.

Loudness tells us how loud or quiet a sound is.

Some sounds are used as warnings or alarms. They are often loud and high pitched, like a police siren or a burglar alarm. These sounds stand out and attract our attention.

Whispers are quiet and low pitched. Only people close by are supposed to hear them.

1 Make a list of all of the sources of sound in this street.

2 Some of the sounds in the picture are useful to us. Other sounds are unpleasant and annoying.

   Underline all of the useful sounds on your list.

   Draw a circle around all of the unpleasant sounds.

3 Sort your sound words into lists.

   Make a list of high pitched sounds and a list of low pitched sounds.

   Make a list of loud sounds and a list of quiet sounds.

4 Write a sentence to explain what these words mean

   | source   pitch |

How sounds are made

All sounds are made by something moving to and fro. This is called vibrating.

When you pluck a guitar string it begins to vibrate. The vibrating string makes the air around it vibrate. The moving air makes the sound.

When you blow across the top of a bottle, the air inside the bottle vibrates. When the vibrations stop, the sound stops too.

The instruments in the picture make their sounds in different ways. The trumpet and recorder are played by blowing.

1 Sort the instruments into groups which are played in the same way.

   Describe how each group of instruments is played.

2 For each group write down what is vibrating to make the sound.

3 Now think about human sounds. Where does the sound come from when you speak? Which part of you is vibrating?

Making different sounds

Musical instruments can usually make more than one sound. There are different ways of changing the pitch of the sounds.

To change the pitch of a sound you must change the vibrating part in some way.

Long strings on a guitar make low sounds.
If you make the vibrating part of the string shorter, you will make the sound higher.

Thin strings make high sounds.
Thick strings make low sounds.

When you play a recorder or a trumpet, the air inside the tube vibrates.

You can change the length of the recorder tube by closing the holes with your fingers.

The longer the tube is, the lower the sound will be.

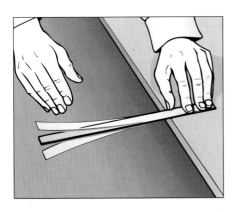
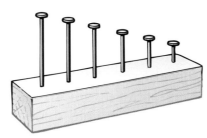

1 Choose two things from this page. Describe how you would make high and low sounds.

2 Do quick vibrations or slow vibrations make the lowest sound?

3 Draw an imaginary musical instrument. Explain how it is played. Label the parts that vibrate to make the sound. Explain how the pitch can be changed.

Sound travels

You hear sounds because vibrations can travel from the source to your ears. Travelling vibrations are called **waves.**

When you call to someone, the vibrations in your voicebox make the air vibrate. We call this a sound **wave**.

The vibrations of the sound wave travel through the air. As they travel they spread out and get weaker. The further they go the weaker they get, and the sound

Years ago, people in different rooms of a big house, or on a ship, talked to each other using 'speaking tubes'.

These children are using a speaking tube made from a long hose pipe. The tubing stops the sound waves from spreading out, so the sound of their voices does not get quieter as the sound wave travels down the tube.

We can measure how fast sound travels. Sound waves travel 330 metres in a second through air. This is the speed of sound.

Sound travels very fast, but light travels even faster.

In a thunderstorm, the flash of lightning and the clap of thunder both happen at the same time. But we can see the lightning before we hear the thunder.

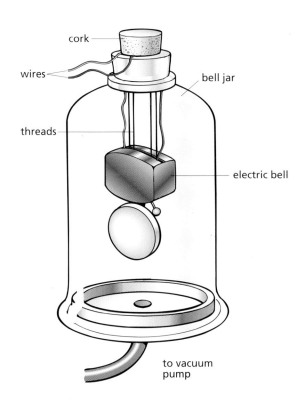

What happens with no air?

In this experiment, when the jar is full of air you can hear the bell ringing.

We can use a pump to take the air out of the jar.

When there is no air in something it is called a **vacuum**. The sound stops because sound cannot travel through a vacuum.

To hear the sound again, air has to be put back into the jar.

1 Why do sounds get fainter as you move away from their source?

2 Why do you see lightning before you hear the thunder.

3 How long will it take the sound to reach you if the storm is 990 metres away?

4 Why can no sound be heard in a vacuum?

5 An explosion in space would make no sound. Explain why this is.

Keeping sound out

These people are working in very noisy places.

Very loud noise can damage the delicate parts of the ear. This could cause deafness.

Workers should wear ear protectors to prevent loud sounds from damaging their ears.

Ear protectors work by absorbing the sound waves which pass through them from the outside. This means that only some of the sound gets through, so it is not so loud.

The material in an ear protector must be good at stopping sound. This diagram shows how it works.

Because the sound is made quiet, the ear is not damaged.

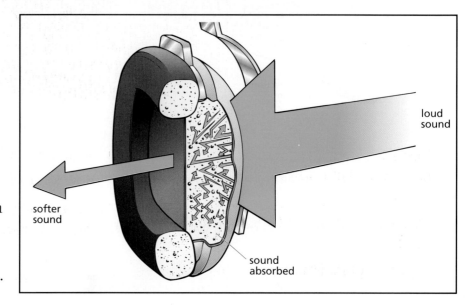

loud sound

softer sound

sound absorbed

Loud sounds

The loudness of a noise is measured in **decibels** (dB).
Some sound levels are shown in the chart below.
Sound levels above 80 decibels can be harmful.
Too much loud sound can damage the ear.

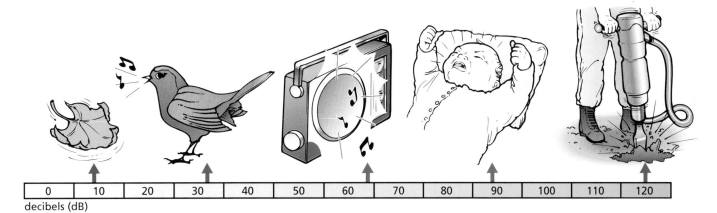

0	10	20	30	40	50	60	70	80	90	100	110	120

decibels (dB)

Car engines make a lot of noise. The bonnet of this car is lined with a material which is good at absorbing sound. This makes the engine sound quieter when you are inside the car.

1   Make a list of jobs which people do where there is a lot of noise.

2   What do you think the noise level would be for these sounds? Write down the answer in decibels.

• watching T.V. inside your home

• at a football match when a goal is scored

• a friend whispering

3   Write a sentence to explain how the noise from a car engine is cut down.

Hearing sounds

Vibrating sound waves can travel through the air to our ears. The vibrations go on travelling inside our ears. We hear the sound when the message gets to our brain.

This diagram shows what happens to the sound waves when they enter your ear.

Vibrations can pass from one material to another.

Small bones in the ear pass the vibrations to the inner ear. Then a nerve takes a message to the brain.

When the messages get to the brain, we hear the sound.

If the delicate parts of the ear are damaged, our hearing may not be as good.

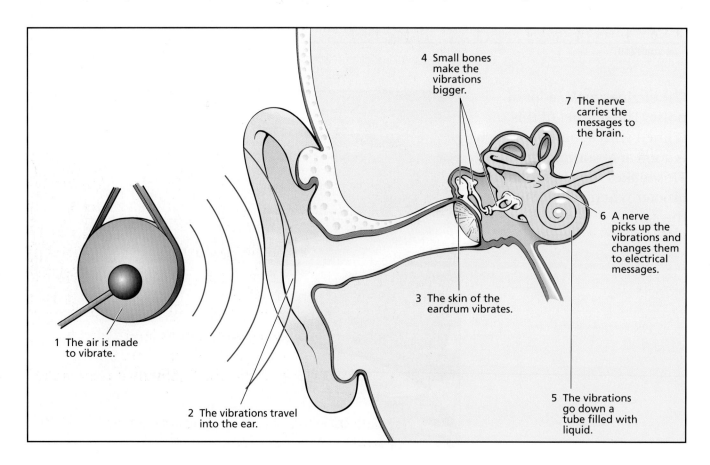

4 Small bones make the vibrations bigger.

7 The nerve carries the messages to the brain.

6 A nerve picks up the vibrations and changes them to electrical messages.

3 The skin of the eardrum vibrates.

1 The air is made to vibrate.

2 The vibrations travel into the ear.

5 The vibrations go down a tube filled with liquid.

1 Write a list of the parts of the ear. Put them in the order that they vibrate when sound goes in.

2 Use the information to make a flow chart to explain how you hear a sound when the vibration enters your ear.

3 Look carefully at the diagram. List three ways in which you think the ear could become damaged to cause deafness.

4 Why is it harmful to be in a very noisy place?

Light all around

In a room which is completely dark we cannot see anything.
Light has to enter our eyes for us to be able to see.
Light travels from a light source.

Using light

Light is very important in our lives. We need light to see things. We also use it to send messages and give warnings.

There are some examples of messages and warnings in this picture.

Some objects make light and send it out as light rays. These are called **luminous** objects or light sources. We can see these objects because the light which they make travels to our eyes.

Most objects do not make their own light. They are **non-luminous**.

1 Make a list of all of the light sources in the street scene.

2 Circle all the light sources on your list that are being used to give messages.

   What messages are they giving?

3 Make a list of some other signs and signals which use light.

4 Write a sentence to explain these words
   - light source
   - luminous

Light passing through

When light leaves a source it travels until it meets an object. Light passes through some materials, but not others.

Glass and Perspex let light pass through. We can see clearly through them. They are called **transparent** materials.

Other materials, like wood, do not let light through. They are **opaque** materials.

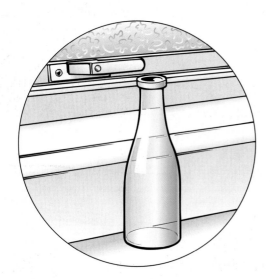

Some things let light through but we can not see through them. These are called **translucent** materials. When light passes through a translucent material the light is spread out in many directions. This stops us from seeing clearly through it.

Look at all the objects in this bathroom.

1 Make a list of those which are:
   • transparent
   • translucent
   • opaque

2 Chose three of the objects.
   What materials are they made of?
   Why do you think that material was chosen?

3 Write in your own words explaining what these words mean:
   • transparent
   • translucent
   • opaque

Making shadows

Opaque objects do not let light pass through. When light hits these objects, **shadows** form behind them.
The shadow shows where light passed by their edges.

To make shadows you need a light source and some opaque objects.

You can change the size of a shadow by moving the objects closer to the light or the screen. The nearer the object is to the light, the bigger the shadow will be.

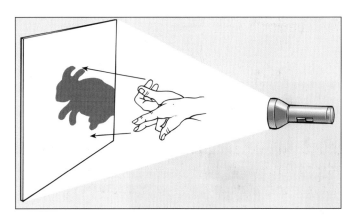

1 Explain how you think a shadow is made. The diagram above may help you.

2 What happens to the light which hits the opaque object?

3 Explain how you can make the shadow of an object get bigger or smaller.

4 Why do shadows have clear sharp edges?

Light travels

Light leaving a source travels away in all directions.
It travels as **light rays**.

Light travels in **light rays**. Each of these pictures shows that light rays travel in straight lines. This is easy to see if you have a strong light source. But even if you cannot see it, light from all sources always travels in straight lines.

This girl can see through the straight tubing, but not the bent tubing. This is because light can not get round the bend in the tubing to reach her eye.

1 Write a sentence about how we know that light rays can only travel in straight lines.

2 How does the tubing experiment show that light travels in straight lines?

3 Draw a diagram of a light bulb.
Draw lines to show the rays of light coming out of the bulb.

Seeing things

We need light to see things. Light from a source must enter our eyes so that we can see it. We see other objects when light bounces off them and enters our eyes.

How do we see things?

Light rays travel from a source.

When light hits an object some of the light bounces back off it. This is called a **reflection.** We can see things when light which has been reflected by them enters our eyes.

The light makes a picture in our eyes of what we are looking at. The eyes send a message to our brain. We 'see' something when the message gets to our brain.

All materials reflect light, but some reflect more than others.
A white material, such as the paper of this book, reflects a lot of light.
A dark material, such as a black coat, does not reflect much light.
White or pale clothing is best for being seen at night because it reflects a lot of light.

Which is the best reflector?

When light is reflected from a surface, it bounces off in all directions. We say the light is scattered.

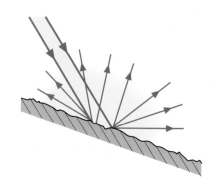

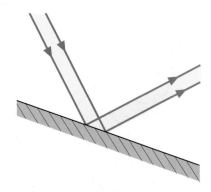

Shiny materials do not spread the light out very much when it is reflected. They keep the rays together in a single light beam. Shiny objects make very good reflectors.

Not all of the light is reflected. Some may be absorbed by the material. Materials which absorb a lot of light are not good reflectors.

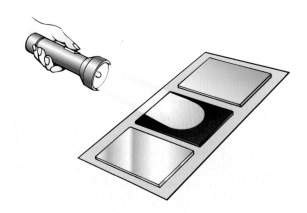

Reflective clothing is made of material which reflects a lot of light, and so it can be seen even when there is not much light about.

1 Write a sentence to explain what these words mean:
   • reflect
   • absorb

2 Why is it a good idea to wear light coloured clothes on a dark night?

3 Why are shiny surfaces good reflectors?

Mirrors and light

Some surfaces are very good at reflecting light.
A glass mirror has a shiny metal backing which always reflects light beams the same way.

We can always **predict** which way a reflected lightbeam will go. We can use mirrors to send light beams where we want them.

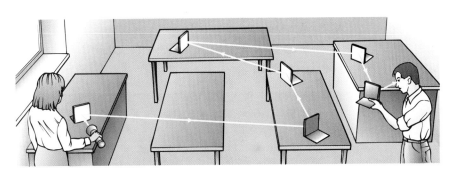

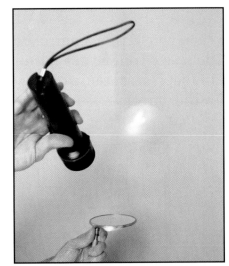

When a light beam hits a flat mirror at an angle it always bouces off at an equal angle in the other direction.

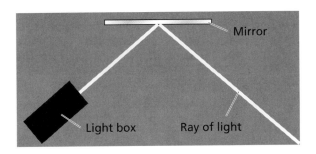

Mirror

Light box   Ray of light

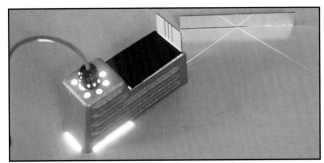

Reflections work best with a straight beam of light that does not spread out.

A laser produces a strong, straight beam of light that does not spread out.

Mirrors are used to control the laser beams in light shows like this one.

1 Write down two ways in which mirrors can be used to control the direction of light beams.

2 Draw a diagram to show what happens to a ray of light when it hits a mirror.

3 Write a sentence to explain how the light beam is reflected by the mirror.

Looking in mirrors

Mirrors produce a picture, or **image**, of what is in front of them. But the mirror image is not quite the same as the real thing.

When you look in a mirror, what you see is called an **image**.
The image you see in a mirror always looks back-to-front.
This happens because of the way light rays are reflected by the mirror.

We can see mirror images in other shiny surfaces too. These images are called '**reflections**'.

Writing that is back-to-front is called mirror writing. It looks impossible to read.

Mirror writing is used on the front of some vehicles. It can be read by the driver in a car in front. The driver sees the writing in the car mirror.

You can use mirror writing to send secret messages to a friend.
Here is an example to try.
Hold the writing in front of a mirror if you want to read it.

Go for Science

When you use more than one mirror, the images can be reflected backwards and forwards between the mirrors.

This can produce amazing effects. Try and see how many images you can get.

Curved mirrors, like those in fun fairs, give interesting images too.

Periscopes

Periscopes are made with two mirrors. They can bend light round corners. You can use a periscope to see over heads in a crowd.

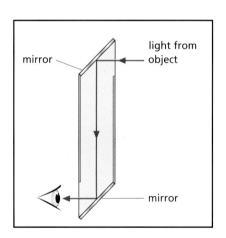

mirror

light from object

mirror

1 Here is some mirror writing. What does the sign say?

2 Where might you see a sign written like this? Where would you see its reflection?

3 Look at your reflection in a spoon. Draw a picture of your face. How is the image changed?

Day and night

The Sun is a giant ball of hot gases which gives off light and heat. The light from the Sun is our daylight. The Sun is a light source.

During the daytime, the Sun appears to move across the sky, rising in the east and going down in the west. Shadows made by the Sun also move as the day passes.

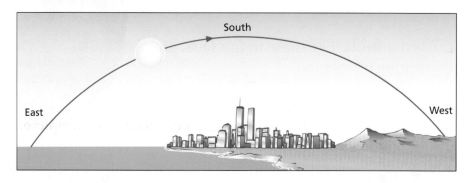

The Sun does not really move across the sky. It just seems to move to us because the Earth is spinning around. When we stand on the Earth and look at the Sun, it is really us who are moving.

When the Sun shines on our part of the Earth it is daytime. At night our part of the Earth is turned away from the Sun.

1 Make a drawing of the tree in the picture, showing its shadow in the morning, and in the evening.

2 Write a sentence explaining why the tree shadow moved position.

3 Draw a diagram to show how the Earth's movement causes day and night.

The changing moon

The moon looks bright at night, but it is not a light source. The light we see is sunlight being reflected by the moon onto the Earth.

The moon appears to move across the sky each night. This happens because the Earth is spinning. As the Earth turns around each night, it looks to us as if the moon is moving.

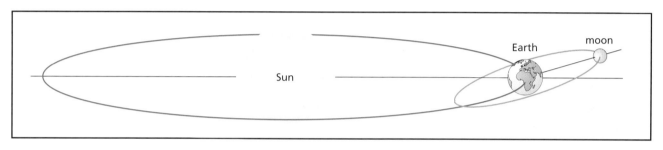

The moon also moves. It travels around the Earth. Each journey round the Earth is called an **orbit.** Each orbit takes 28 days to complete.

The shape of the moon seems to change each night. The moon is always round, but we do not always see all of it. We only see the part which reflects light from the Sun. The 'full moon' is when all of its sunny side is facing the Earth. When only part of the sunny side is facing the Earth, we only see the shape of the sunny part.

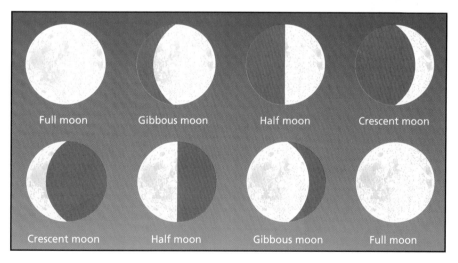

Full moon   Gibbous moon   Half moon   Crescent moon

Crescent moon   Half moon   Gibbous moon   Full moon

1 Draw a diagram showing the Sun, Earth and moon. Show how the moon reflects light from the Sun to the Earth.

2 Why does the moon seem to move across the sky each night?

3 Draw the different shapes we see as the moon 'changes'. Does it really change?

4 What does the word 'orbit' mean? How long does it take for the moon to orbit the Earth?

Stars

On a clear night you can see thousands of stars in the sky. Each star is a source of light. Some stars look brighter than others.

The stars are so far away from us that light takes many years to make the journey to Earth. In one year, light can travel 9.5 million kilometres. This distance is called a light year. Even the closest star is over four light years away from the Earth.

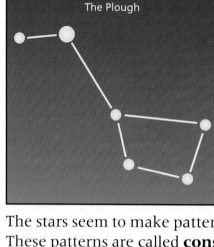

The Plough

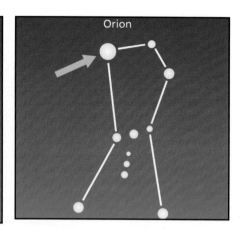

Orion

The stars seem to make patterns in the sky. These patterns are called **constellations**.

During the night the stars appear to move across the sky. They are not really moving, however. They just seem to move because the Earth is spinning.

The brightness of stars is measured on a magnitude scale.

Very bright stars have a magnitude of 1.

Stars which can only just be seen with your eyes have a magnitude of 6.

The star marked with an arrow in the constellation of Orion has a magnitude of 1.

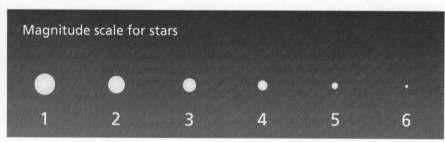

Magnitude scale for stars

1   2   3   4   5   6

1   Why do the stars seem to move across the sky at night?

2   Draw the constellation of Orion. Write next to each star what you think its brightness is, using the magnitude scale.

3   What does a 'light year' mean?

4   Why do some stars look brighter than others?

Materials and Mixtures

Different **materials** have different **properties**.
We look at the properties of a material.
Then we can get the best material for the job.

There are all sorts of things made of different materials at this swimming pool.

The float is a thing made of the light material called polystyrene.

There is a lot of glass at this swimming pool. Two of the properties of glass are –

- Glass is colourless and

- You can see through glass. We say it is transparent.

**Look carefully at the picture. Then finish these sentences.
Use some of the words in the box.**

1 I can see a thing called a . . . .

  made of the material called . . . .

2 Two materials that are hard are . . . .

  and . . . .

3 A material that bends easily is . . . .

4 A material that breaks easily is . . . .

5 Write down the name of another material.

6 Make a list of its properties.

nylon	water
aluminium	ceramic
tile	PVC
glass	wood
rubber	goggles
float	polystyrene

Solids, liquids and gases

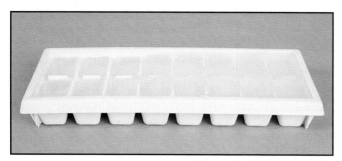

Ice is frozen water.

There is 'condensation' on the window. It is liquid water.

Water boils at 100°C. When water boils some of it changes to a gas. The gas is water **vapour**. We often call water vapour 'steam'.

Write the answers to these questions in your book.

1 Look at the picture of the swimming pool. on page 41

Find one liquid.

Find two gases. You will need to look very hard!

Find three solids.

2 Draw your own picture and label these –

three solids

three liquids

three gases.

3 Match these words with the sentences below.

solid	liquid	gas

It keeps its shape on its own . . . .

It is easy to squash. . . . .

It is runny . . . .

4 Now make up your own sentences for these answers.

It . . . . (solid)

It . . . . (liquid)

It . . . . (gas)

Gases

We can smell some gases even if we are not close to them. This is because the tiny particles in the gas can move about quickly.

MM3

particles

Mmm! delicious

When food is being cooked the smell of the food moves away from the kitchen. The smell is a gas.

A gas is made of lots and lots of tiny particles that are moving all the time.

We smell the gas when the particles reach our nose.

The particles move through the air. You know they have reached your nose when you can smell the curry.

The way the gas particles spread is called **diffusion**.

The particles move from one place to another until they are all spread out evenly.

The particles in the 'curry' gas mix with the particles in the air.

The same thing happens in this experiment with coloured gas.

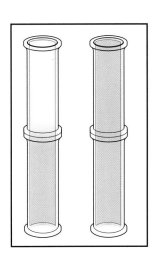

At first there are lots of nitrogen dioxide particles at the bottom of the jar but they move about fast. After some time they will fill both jars.

We can tell when this has happened because we can see the brown colour in both jars.

Finish these sentences.

1   We can think of a gas as being made up of lots of . . . .

    They are moving very . . . .

2   Write a few sentences to explain how cooking smells move from the kitchen. Use these words –

    | diffusion   particles   fast   mix |

3   Draw two diagrams of the gas jars in the picture of the nitrogen dioxide experiment. Use brown spots for nitrogen dioxide particles.

    Add nitrogen dioxide particles to the jars to show where the nitrogen dioxide particles are at first.

    In the second diagram, show where the nitrogen dioxide particles have travelled to after some time.

Solids and liquids

The particles in a solid stay close together. The particles in a liquid touch each other but they can move about. The particles in a gas move fast and can spread out.

The particles in a liquid can move about and change places. But they do not move as fast as gas particles do.

The particles in a solid do not move about.They can only move a little bit. But they do shake all the time. We call this shaking 'vibration'.

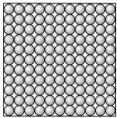

particles in a solid–
these are vibrating
'moving on the spot'

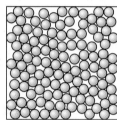

particles in a liquid–
these can move about

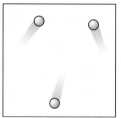

particles in a gas–
these are moving
really fast

steam

water

ice

Gaseous petrol
(fumes of petrol)

No smoking

Switch off
engine

Petroleum
spirit highly
flammable

liquid petrol

solid rubber

WPC 193Y

Look at the picture of a car being filled with petrol.

1 What can you see that tells you the particles in a liquid move easily?

2 How can you tell that the particles of a gas move away from the pump?.

3 How can you tell that particles in a solid hardly move at all?

4 Write (or draw) yourself some hints to help you remember what the particles are like in

a solid

a liquid

a gas.

Evaporation

When a liquid turns into a gas we call it **evaporation**. When the gas turns back to a liquid we call it **condensation**.

Evaporation is happening all the time.

When washing dries, the water disappears from the washing. It goes into the air.

The water has changed from liquid water in the wet washing to water vapour in the air. When a liquid changes to a gas we say it has evaporated.

Condensation is the opposite of evaporation.

We cannot see water vapour in the air, but it is often there. When water vapour touches a cold surface it turns into liquid water. This is the 'condensation' we see on a cold window.

Water vapour is not the only gas that condenses. Condensation happens when any gas turns to liquid.

1 These pictures show evaporation and condensation. Work out which picture shows which. Write your answers in a table like this. The first one is done for you. Then add two more ideas of your own.

What I can see in the picture	Evaporation or condensation
Washing drying	Evaporation
. . . .	. . . .
. . . .	. . . .
. . . .	. . . .
. . . .	. . . .

2 Finish these sentences. Use these words —

> condensation   evaporation

a) When a liquid turns to a gas we call it
   . . . .

b) When a gas turns to a liquid we call it
   . . . .

c) The opposite of condensation is called
   . . . .

d) When water vapour touches a cold surface and turns to liquid it is called. . . . .

Boiling

When a liquid boils lots of big bubbles form. These bubbles go up to the surface of the liquid and then burst. **Pure** liquids boil at just one temperature. This is the **boiling** point of the liquid.

When we buy cooked food to reheat we should read the label. The label may say 'Do not boil' because boiling will spoil the food. But it is important to make the food really hot. We need to know what boiling is, so that we do not let the food boil.

Some people think that as soon as they see any bubbles in the liquid it is boiling. This is wrong. A liquid only boils properly when lots of big bubbles come up to the surface of the liquid and burst.

If we boil a pure liquid the temperature stays the same until all the liquid has boiled away. Pure water boils at 100°C.

When a liquid boils, the particles inside the liquid make bubbles of gas. When the bubbles burst, the gas particles go into the air.

Here are some differences between boiling and evaporation.

Boiling   Evaporation

Finish these sentences about boiling. Use these words.

boiling gas pure quickly boiling

1 Boiling is what happens when we heat a liquid and it turns to a . . . .

2 A pure liquid boils at one temperature. We call this the . . . . point.

3 When a liquid boils the particles leave the liquid and move a lot more . . . .

4 100°C is the boiling point of . . . . water

5 What is the missing word on the arrow?

(. . . . .)

Liquid ⟶ Gas

Freezing and melting

Freezing is what happens when a liquid turns to a solid.
Melting is what happens when a solid turns to a liquid.

Sometimes we say we are 'freezing'. What we really mean is that we are very cold. Real freezing is different.

Freezing means that a liquid has changed into a solid. The particles in the liquid move more and more slowly as they get colder.

'I'm freezing'

After a time the particles are very close together and only just moving, or *vibrating*. The liquid has turned into a solid.

If the substance is pure, the temperature stays the same while it is freezing. We call this temperature the freezing point.

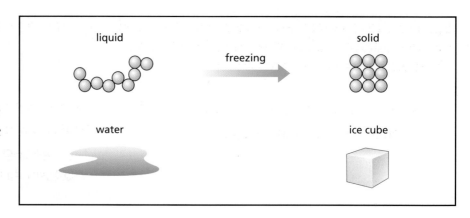

liquid
freezing
solid
water
ice cube

The opposite happens when we warm a solid. The particles move about more and more and after a time all the solid turns to a liquid.

When it melts, a solid substance loses its shape. When the substance is liquid it will fit into any container.

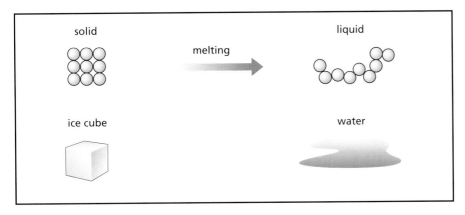

When a solid turns into a liquid we call it melting. This happens at exactly the same temperature as freezing would for that substance. So if you know the freezing point of a substance you also know its melting point.

Remember that when a substance melts from a solid to a liquid, it is still the same substance.
It is *not* a new, different substance.

Each of these sentences has a mistake in it. Find the mistake.
(It may help to look at the underlined parts.)
Then write the sentence correctly.

1 Freezing is when a liquid turns to a <u>gas</u>.
2 The opposite of melting is <u>boiling</u>.

3 When a solid melts we get <u>a different</u> substance formed.
4 The melting point and <u>boiling</u> point of a substance are the same.

Mixtures and pure substances

A pure substance is all made of the same 'stuff'. It has one melting point and one boiling point.
A **mixture** contains several pure substances put together.

It is often important to make things pure.

Neon is one of the substances in air. Neon is used in advertising signs to make them glow bright red. If the sign is filled with air then it will not glow red.

Most things that we see each day are mixtures. Air, rocks, soil, sea water, oil, wood, glass, milk and a cup of tea are all mixtures.

Mixtures contain different substances. For example the air around you contains these substances –

nitrogen
oxygen
argon,
water vapour
carbon dioxide
helium
neon
krypton

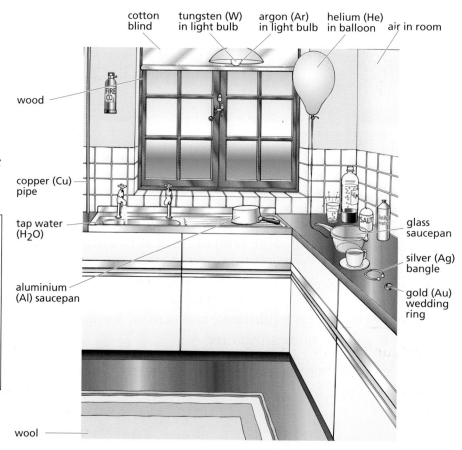

Some everyday things are pure substances. If a substance is pure it can be written in shorthand. H_2O is the symbol for pure water.

Look at the picture carefully and write down the names of these things

1 A pure substance that is a solid

2 A pure substance that is a liquid

3 A pure substance that is a gas.

4 A mixture of a gas in a liquid.

5 A mixture of gases.

Soluble and insoluble

Some **solids** dissolve in water to make a **solution**. When this happens we call the solid a **solute** and the water a **solvent**.

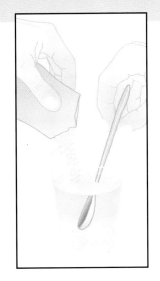

Water is called a solvent because it can dissolve some solids.

When the orange drink powder is added to the water it dissolves. We can call the orange drink powder a solute.

orange drink powder	+ water	makes orange drink
solute	+ solvent	makes solution
(the substance that dissolves)	(the substance that does the dissolving)	(the mixture)

Water is the most common solvent.

There are many other solvents that are very useful to us.

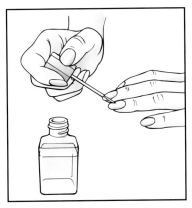

The nail varnish in the bottle is a solution.

With some paint the brushes need to be cleaned using hot soapy water.

The colour in the nail varnish is the solute. When the nail varnish is painted on the nails the solvent evaporates and leaves the colour on the nails.

But some paint does not dissolve in water. Then the paintbrushes have to be cleaned with a special liquid paintbrush cleaner. The paintbrush cleaning liquid is a solvent that dissolves the paint.

1 Write your own meaning for these words –
   a) solute
   b) solvent
   c) solution.

2 Find the names of two solutes, two solvents and two solutions on this page. Try and think of two of your own. Write your answers in a table like this one.

	2 on page	2 of my own
solute		
solvent		
solution		

Dissolving

When solids dissolve in solvents they seem to disappear.
But they are still there.

Sea water has salt dissolved in it. It tastes salty if you get some in your mouth.

Washing powders contain lots of different ingredients.

One of the ingredients in washing powder is *detergent*.
It is needed to dissolve the grease on our clothes.

Other ingredients help to make the colours of the clothes stay bright.

It is important that all the ingredients dissolve well.

Sometimes washing powder is used in boiling water. Sometimes it is used in cooler water. It must dissolve well at all the different temperatures.

FABRIC CARE INFORMATION
Wash mixed loads according to temperature/gentlest cycle, labelled article.
Always follow any special instructions such as "wash separately".

WASH CYCLE AND WASH TEMPERATURE	
95° 60° 40°	Wash in machine up to the temperature mentioned
60° 40°	Synthetics or permanent press programme only
40°	Wool cycle only
⊠	Do not wash or wet
✋	Hand wash only

Many substances dissolve better when the solvent is hotter.

Dissolving sugar

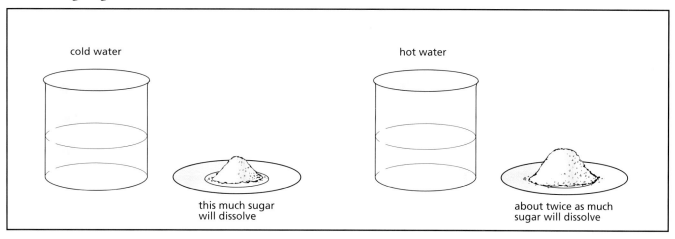

cold water

this much sugar
will dissolve

hot water

about twice as much
sugar will dissolve

Different solids will dissolve by different amounts in a solvent

Dissolving salt and sugar

salt in hot water

not much
dissolves

sugar in hot water

a lot dissolves

We say that sugar is more **soluble** than salt.

Scientists have to work out the **solubility** of each ingredient in a washing powder.
A washing powder with **insoluble** ingredients would not sell well.

1   What is the solvent for washing powder?

2   Sugar dissolves in water. How much sugar
    dissolves when we make the water hotter?

3   Imagine we have two beakers of water at
    60°C. Can we dissolve more salt or more
    sugar?

4   Write this sentence in your own words –
    'Sugar has a greater solubility than salt'.

5   Jane says that she can get the salt back out
    of a salt solution. Is she correct or has the
    salt changed into a new substance?

Filtering

A lot of substances are mixtures with different bits in them. You can separate the 'bits' from the mixture. There are many ways of doing this.

We get our chemical substances from raw materials.

Lots of these raw materials come from rocks, oil and air.

Rocks, oil and air are examples of mixtures.

Iron is a useful metal that we can get from rocks.

Salt can be taken out of sea water.

There is a lot of nitrogen in air. Nitrogen is used to make fertiliser.

We have to be able to separate the parts of a mixture so that we can get the substances that we need.

One way of separating the parts in a mixture is by filtering it.

We use this method to separate a solid from a liquid. If you have ever strained the peas at home you have already done some filtering.

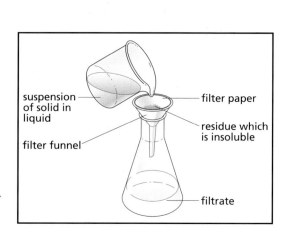

Look carefully at the picture of filtering. Then complete these sentences. These words may help you —

| insoluble residue filtrate suspension |

1

The liquid that goes through the filter is called the ....

2 The solid that stays on the filter paper is called the ....

3 We can separate substances by filtering if we have a .... which is mixed up in a liquid.

4 We say the solid is .... in water.

Mixing and separating

We can use a separating funnel to separate liquids that do not mix.

Some liquids do not mix when we put them together. We can see different layers.

We say the two liquids are **immiscible**. This happens when oil and water are put together. We can separate the two liquids by pouring off the top layer.

We may do this when we make gravy at home. It is not very easy to do. Some of the oil gets left behind.

A better way of separating liquids is with a separating funnel.

First we open the tap to let the bottom liquid out, then we close the tap. When we open the tap again the liquid that was in the upper layer comes out.

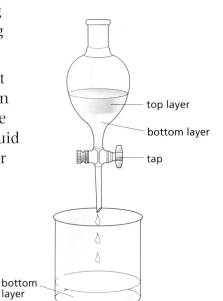

- top layer
- bottom layer
- tap
- bottom layer

- oil (top layer)
- gravy (bottom layer)

You may have a sort of separating funnel at home. It might be in a kitchen cupboard. It is a special jug for pouring gravy.

1 Finish these sentences so that they explain what the underlined words mean.

a) If two liquids are <u>immiscible</u> they

....

b) A <u>separating funnel</u> is used

to...

2 Some yellow oil has been spilt into a bottle of black ink.

Describe how to separate the yellow oil and the black ink using a separating funnel.

You could draw a diagram and label it.

3 Name two liquids that cannot be separated by using a separating funnel.

.... and

....

Write a sentence about why it would not work for these liquids.

Distillation

Distillation is used to get the solvent back from a solution.

Distillation happens when a liquid evaporates into a gas and then the gas condenses back to a liquid.

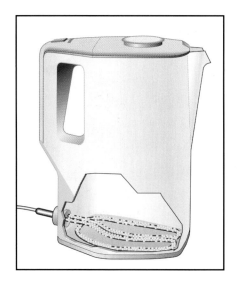

Sometimes we need very pure water. The water from the tap is not always pure enough. You may have seen some of the impurities in the water. They are left inside the kettle after the water has boiled.

We use apparatus like the one opposite to distil pure water from tap water.

The pure water that is collected is called the **distillate**.

Distillation has been used for a very long time. This German distillation apparatus was used in AD 1500.

Distillation is used to make petrol, medicines, perfume and spirits such as whisky.

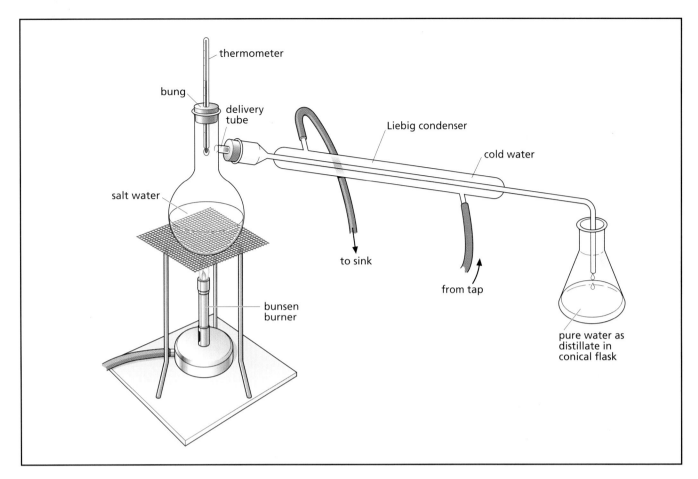

The water is heated and some of it evaporates.

The gas from the water goes up inside the container. It then goes down the delivery tube.

Cold water surrounds the inner tube in the Liebig condenser. The water vapour in the inner tube condenses back into liquid water.

This drips down the tube and is collected in a flask.

1   Look at the distillation apparatus carefully. Write down what these parts do.

a) Bunsen burner

b) Delivery tube

c) Bung

d) Condenser

e) Conical flask

2   Imagine that you are on a hot sunny island. There is no fresh water. There is only sea water. There are palm trees with big, tough, shiny leaves. There are also some cold rocks that you have dug up from the sand . You have found three tins and two plastic bottles on the beach.

Explain how you could get some water that you could drink.

– Think about how you will heat the water so that it evaporates.

– Think how you will cool the gas to give you pure water.

– You could draw some pictures to help you explain.

Chromatography

Chromatography is used to get pure colours from a mixture of colours.

Colours used for felt tip pens, paints, ink and food colours are made of mixtures of coloured dyes. Often, the colours are dissolved in water. Sometimes they are dissolved in a solvent such as alcohol.

We can separate the colours from the mixture by chromatography.

This picture shows one way of doing this.

The water moves up the paper and takes the colours with it. The colour that dissolves the easiest moves the furthest.

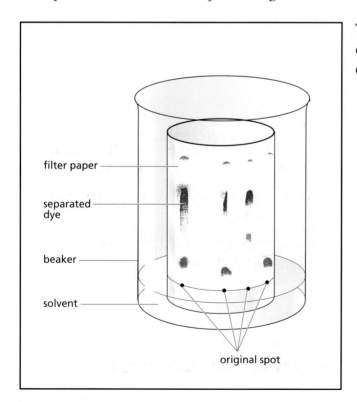

filter paper

separated dye

beaker

solvent

original spot

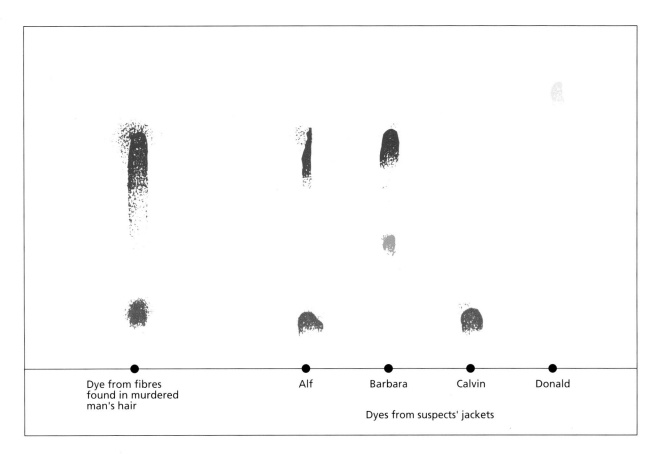

Dye from fibres found in murdered man's hair	Alf	Barbara	Calvin	Donald

Dyes from suspects' jackets

The police can use chromatography to get more evidence about a crime.

This chromatogram shows some dyes. The dyes are from fibres left by a burglar. You can also see the dyes from fibres in some other people's jackets. The police can match the dyes and prove who was at the scene of the crime.

Finish these sentences.

Use some of these words –

Alf Barbara Calvin dissolves
Donald evaporates mixtures
nurse one pure substance
two policeman

1 We use chromatography to get pure colours from ....

2 To do chromatography we need a liquid which .... the colours.

3 Someone who might use chromatography in their work is a ....

4 The number of pure colours used in the burglar's jacket was ....

5 a) The burglar might be ....

b) I think this because

....

(use your own words to anwer 5b)

Rock salt

Rock salt is a very useful substance. It is mined and then purified.

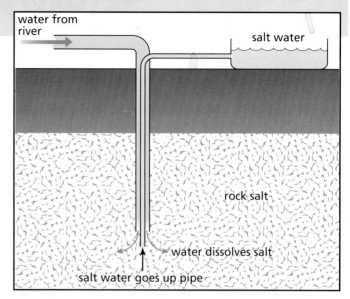

When there were dinosaurs living in this country there were large salt lakes. This was about 150 million years ago. These salt lakes dried up and were buried below a lot of soil and rocks.

We think that these salt lakes were about 400 metres below the surface about 20,000 years ago. Large mammals were living then.

Now we have to dig a mine to get salt from deep in the ground. There is a lot of salt beneath parts of North and Central England.

Water is pumped into the ground. The water dissolves the salt but does not dissolve the rock. The salt solution is pumped back up to the surface.

Salt has lots of uses.

Most of the salt is used for de-icing roads.

It is also used to make –
hydrogen
chlorine (for swimming pools)

A lot of pure salt is used in foods.

1 Finish these sentences.

Use some of these words –

| boiled | evaporated |
| soluble | insoluble |

a) The salt lakes dried up. The water must have .... into the air.

b) Salt is .... in water.

c) The rock stays under the ground. The rock is............... in water.

A new life

The birth of a baby is a special day – or night!
A new life has started.
Babies need a lot of looking after.

HH1

These babies are about one hour old. They have grown for forty weeks inside their mother.

They will be looked after by their parents.

They must be kept warm and clean.

They need the right type of food to help them grow and be healthy.

They will need lots of attention and help as they learn new things.

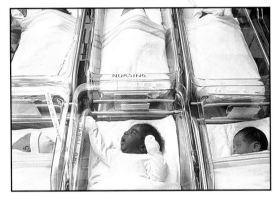

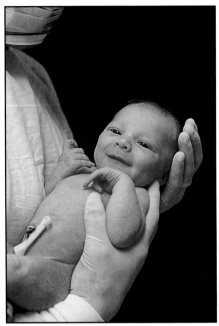

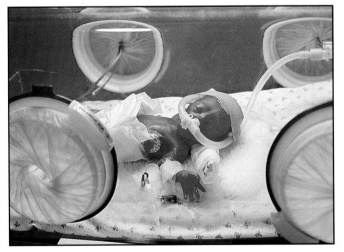

This baby was born after growing inside her mother for only twenty-six weeks.
She is very small.

She is being looked after in an **incubator**. This helps to keep her warm.

She is being fed liquids through a tube.

1 How many weeks does a baby normally grow inside its mother before it is born?

2 Write a list of five things a newborn baby can do.

3 Write three things that a baby needs to help it grow and be healthy.

4 Why are some babies looked after in incubators?

5 What does an incubator do for the baby?

Feeding time

A baby needs to be fed every few hours.
Food contains things which help us to grow.
We get energy from food too.

The milk which a new baby feeds on contains many substances. The baby needs these to stay alive and be healthy. We call these substances **nutrients**.

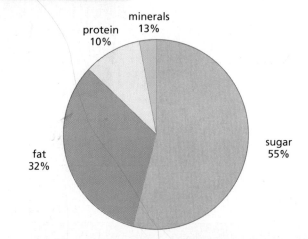

These are some of the nutrients in milk –

Carbohydrate, such as sugar, gives the baby energy.

Fat also gives energy.

Protein is for the baby to grow.

Calcium is for healthy bones and teeth.

Vitamins help the body work properly and keep away disease.

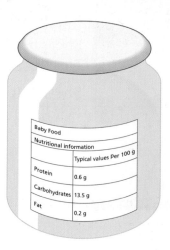

This chart show how much of each substance is in breast milk.

The list on the baby food pack tells you what nutrients it contains.

1 Write down three reasons why a baby needs food.

2 What substances in food give energy?

3 What substance in food is needed for the baby to grow?

4 What is calcium needed for?

5 Write a list of substances in breast milk.

A healthy diet

To be healthy, we need to eat a mixture of different types of food. The mixture should contain enough of each of the substances our bodies need.

These foods contain a lot of carbohydrate.

These foods contain a lot of protein.

These foods contain a lot of fat.

These foods contain a lot of vitamins.

You also need fibre from your food. Fibre helps food to move through your gut. There is a lot of fibre in vegetables and cereals.

The food which we eat each day is called our diet.

Eating the right mixture of all of the nutrients we need is called a *balanced diet*. The mother's milk provides a baby with a balanced diet.

Eating a balanced diet will keep you healthy.
You will get the nutrients you need to grow and be active.

Here are two balanced meals

A diet that is not balanced is unhealthy.
If you eat too little fruit and vegetables you may not get enough vitamins.

If you eat too many sweets or too much fatty food you could become overweight.
These high energy foods are made into fat in your body.
Too much sugar can also cause tooth decay.

1 Write a list of three foods which contain a lot of protein.

2 Write a list of three foods which contain a lot of carbohydrate.

3 What does the word 'diet' mean?

4 What food would you choose for a healthy meal? Write a list of all the different foods in it. Explain why the meal is healthy.

5 Why is milk a good food for babies?

6 Eating a lot of sweets is bad for your health. Write down two reasons why sweets are bad for you.

Safe food

The food we eat must be clean and free from dangerous **bacteria**. Bacteria are **micro-organisms**. Micro-organisms are tiny living things which can only be seen through a microscope.

Bacteria can get on food in lots of ways.

They grow quickly in warm, damp places.

They can make food 'go bad'.

Some kinds of bacteria can cause disease if they get into our bodies.

Food poisoning is a disease which is caused by bacteria.

If you eat food containing a lot of dangerous bacteria they make poisonous substances inside you body. The poison makes you ill.

Salmonella is one type of bacteria which makes food go bad.

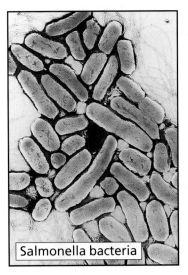

Salmonella bacteria

1 What are bacteria?

2 Draw a picture of salmonella bacteria.

3 What disease do salmonella bacteria cause?

4 Look at the picture of the kitchen. Write down five things which could cause food to become unsafe to eat.

5 Write three rules for keeping food safe in the kitchen.

Keeping clean

Bacteria are microorganisms. Some of them cause diseases.
They can be killed by some substances.

Spots are caused by bacteria. They can be cured by careful cleaning.

A dirty bottle could have bacteria in it. Babies' bottles must be specially cleaned.

Bacteria can reproduce very quickly in a warm place.

Just a few can turn into millions in one day.

If they get in your body they may make you ill.

Bacteria can grow on work surfaces in a kitchen.

These must be kept clean.

Disinfectant can kill bacteria.

Washing removes some bacteria.

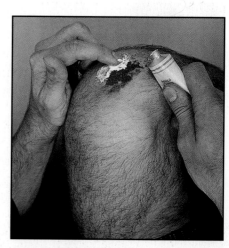

Antiseptic creams stop bacteria growing.

1 What causes spots?

2 Why do babies' bottles have to be specially cleaned?

3 What do antiseptics do?

4 What do disinfectants do?

Antiseptics

An antiseptic is a substance which can kill bacteria. Joseph Lister was the person who discovered this. We sometimes call dangerous bacteria 'germs'.

HH6

Louis Pasteur (1822–1895) was a French scientist. He was the first person to find out that 'germs' were carried by the air. He found out that these bacteria caused illness in people. An illness caused by bacteria is called an infection.

Joseph Lister (1827–1912) was a British doctor. He noticed that many patients died after an operation. Their wounds were infected by bacteria from the air. Lister knew that he needed to kill the bacteria. This would stop them getting into wounds and causing a dangerous infection.

Lister found out that carbolic acid could kill the bacteria. But it did not harm the patients.

He sprayed this antiseptic onto his patients, and into the air, during operations. Many more patients got better.

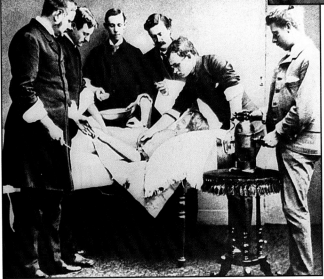

1 How did patients become infected during operations?

2 Write down the name of the antiseptic Joseph Lister used.

3 How did Lister use carbolic acid during operations?

4 Write a sentence to explain what the carbolic acid did to help patients.

A look inside

There are lots of different parts inside our bodies. Each part is called an organ. The organs do jobs which help to keep us alive.

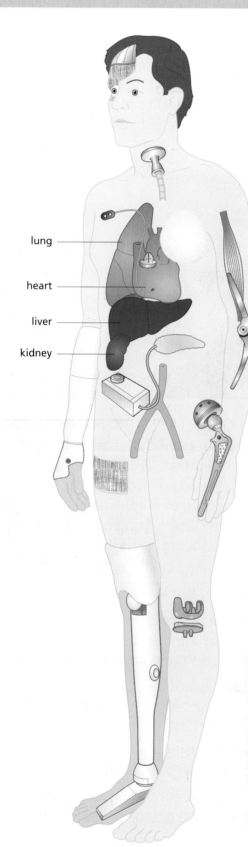

lung

heart

liver

kidney

Sometimes an organ does not work properly. Doctors can replace some organs with artificial ones.

Some organs can be replaced with living parts from another person's body.
This is called an organ transplant.

Doctors used to learn about the organs inside the body by cutting up the bodies of people who had died.

Now doctors can examine organs inside the body without having to cut it open. This helps them to find out if an organ is working properly.

X-rays can pass through the soft parts of our bodies. But the bones inside our body do not let Xrays through. They show up as light areas on an X-ray picture. This X-ray picture shows the bones in the hand. ▶

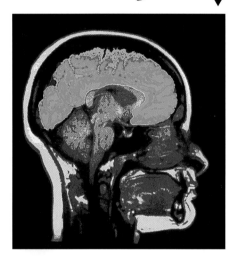

This picture shows a section of a brain. It was made using a scanner. Doctors can use a scanner to look at organs which do not show up on X-ray pictures.
The brain is an organ. ▼

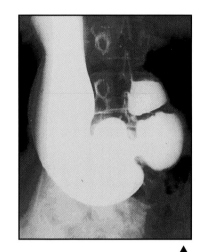

These organs are kidneys. They have been removed from the body of a person who has died in an accident. They are kept cool in ice to keep them alive. They are about to be placed in the body of a person whose own kidneys do not work well. ▼

The stomach cannot normally be seen with X-rays.

This picture was taken after a patient had a drink containing a substance which shows up on an X-ray.
The stomach is an organ.

1 Write a list of the organs inside the body which you know.

2 Write the names of two organs which are inside your chest.

3 Write the names of two organs which are inside your abdomen.

4 Write down the name of the organ which –
a) pumps blood
b) is used when you breathe
c) You see with

5 Write a list of all the ways you know that a doctor can see inside the body.

6 Write the names of the organs that are shown in the pictures.

HH8

Working together

The organs inside your the body work together in groups. Each group of organs is called a system.

Sonia is an athlete. She is in a race.
She needs energy to run.
She gets the energy from the food she has eaten.

She needs oxygen to get the energy from the food. Her lungs take in oxygen when she breathes.

Her blood takes the oxygen and food to her muscles. Her heart pumps blood around her body.

The food reacts with the oxygen in the muscles. The energy from this reaction is used in running.
The muscles use the energy to move bones.
The bones in her legs push her along when she runs.

Organs which work together belong to the same system.

The **respiratory system** puts oxygen into the blood when you breathe.

The **digestive system** moves food around the body.

The **circulatory system** carries blood around the body.

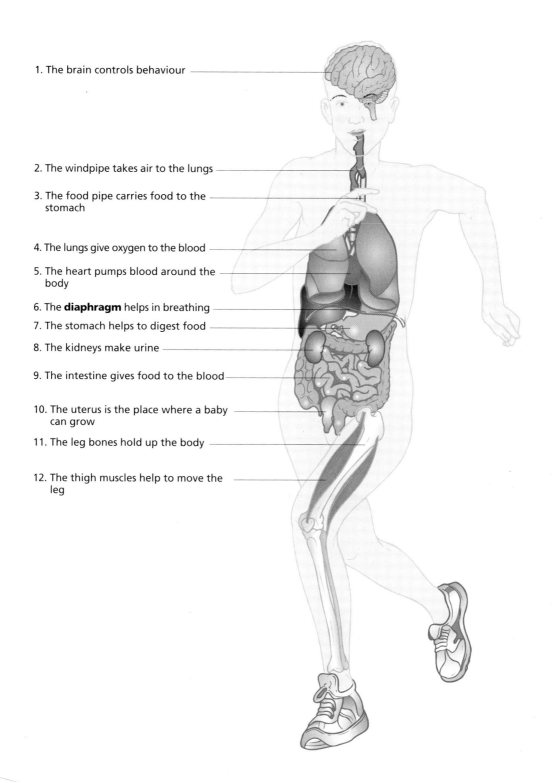

1. The brain controls behaviour

2. The windpipe takes air to the lungs

3. The food pipe carries food to the stomach

4. The lungs give oxygen to the blood

5. The heart pumps blood around the body

6. The **diaphragm** helps in breathing

7. The stomach helps to digest food

8. The kidneys make urine

9. The intestine gives food to the blood

10. The uterus is the place where a baby can grow

11. The leg bones hold up the body

12. The thigh muscles help to move the leg

Look at the picture of the organs inside Sonia's body.

1 Write a list of three organs which help her to breathe. What system do these organs belong to?

2 Write a list of three organs which help her to get food.
What system do these organs belong to?

3 Which parts of her body help her to move?

4 How does she get the energy to run?

Being active

The bones of your skeleton are joined together at joints which can be moved.
The bones are moved by muscles.
Muscles are attached to bones by tendons.
Muscles work by pulling on the bones at a joint.
A muscle gets shorter when it pulls a bone.
This is called contracting.
A muscle uses energy when it **contracts**.
Two muscles are needed to work each joint because a muscle can only pull, it cannot push.

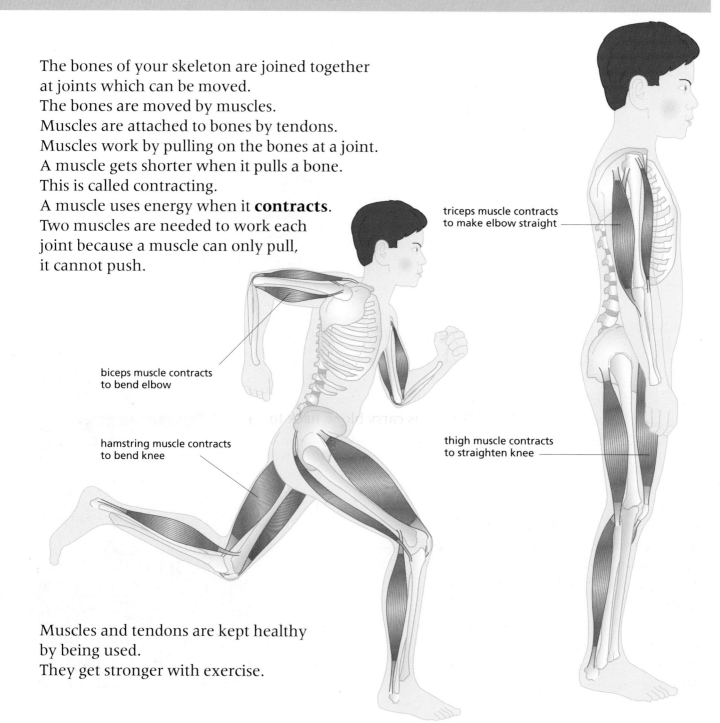

triceps muscle contracts to make elbow straight

biceps muscle contracts to bend elbow

hamstring muscle contracts to bend knee

thigh muscle contracts to straighten knee

Muscles and tendons are kept healthy by being used.
They get stronger with exercise.

1 Write the names of four joints in your body which can move.

2 Write the names of the two muscles which move your arm at the elbow.

3 What job does a tendon do?

4 Write a sentence to explain how a muscle moves a bone.

5 Why is exercise good for muscles?

Active hearts

The heart and blood vessels work together.
They are called the circulatory system.
They move blood around the body.
They take it to all the organs.

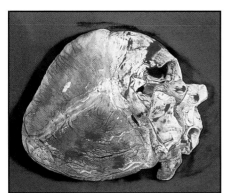

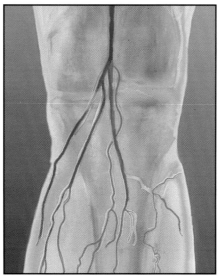

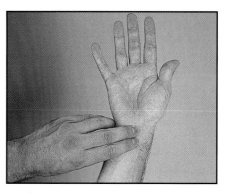

You can feel blood pumping through your artery at your wrist.
This is called a pulse.

The heart is made of muscle. It works like a pump. Each time the heart beats, the muscle pulls tight. It pumps the blood through tubes called arteries.

This picture shows the veins in the leg. A dye has been injected into the veins to make them show up. The veins carry blood back to the heart.

If you do active sports you can make your heart stronger.
It will be able to pump more blood.
Exercise makes you heart beat rate speed up.
People who are fit normally have a low heart beat rate.
After exercise their heart beat rate speeds up but then slows down quickly.
In people who are not fit the heart beats too fast and does not slow down quickly after exercise.
If a person is very overweight the heart has to work harder.
This can cause heart disease.

1 Write a sentence saying what the heart does.

2 Write a sentence saying what a pulse is.

3 Find which parts of your body you can feel a pulse in. Make a list of them.

4 What will happen to the girl's pulse when she is running ?

5 How will this help her body?

Active lungs

When you breathe, air goes in and out of your lungs. This is called the respiratory system. Inside your lungs, oxygen from the air goes into your blood. Carbon dioxide is taken out of your blood and breathed out.

Air has to go through a lot of tubes to get into the lungs. People who do a lot of exercise have healthy lungs. They can take lots of oxygen from the air easily.

Some people suffer from *asthma*. They sometimes find it hard to breathe.
This happens because the tubes in their lungs suddenly become very narrow.
Dust, pollen, animal fur, or exercise may cause an asthma attack.

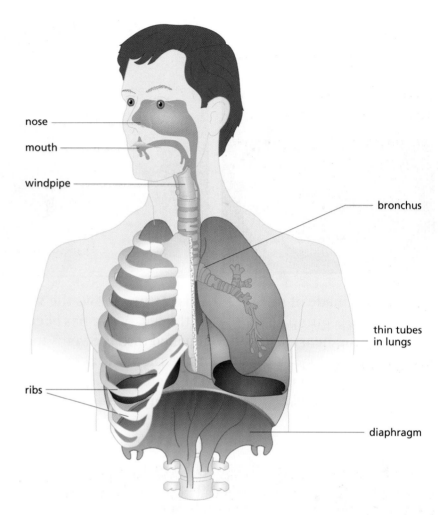

nose
mouth
windpipe
bronchus
thin tubes in lungs
ribs
diaphragm

The drugs in an inhaler stop the tubes in the lungs getting too narrow.
This make it easier for the child to breathe.

1 Place your hands on your chest. Take a deep breath in, and out. What do your ribs do when you breathe?

2 Write the names of the parts of your breathing system which air goes through. The diagram will help.

3 Why do you breathe faster when you run?

4 How does asthma make breathing difficult?

Damaged lungs

Nicotine is a poison. It affects the brain and causes people to become addicted to smoking.
Nicotine makes the arteries narrower, so the heart has to work harder .

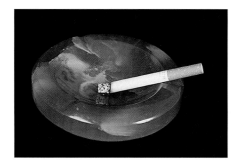

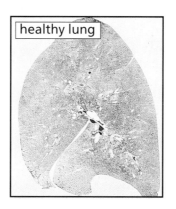

healthy lung

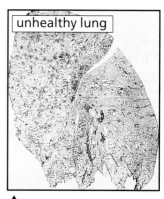

unhealthy lung

Carbon monoxide is a poisonous gas which gets into the blood. It makes it harder for the blood to carry oxygen.

Tar is a sticky brown substance. It collects in the lungs of smokers.
It causes lung cancer which is a deadly disease.

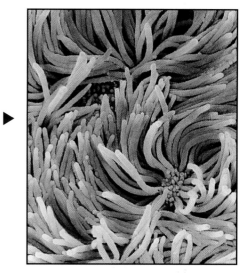

The narrow tubes in the lungs are lined with tiny hairs called cilia. These help to trap the dust and germs we breathe in.
Smoking cigarettes damages these hairs. They cannot do their work properly. The lungs then get blocked up easily.

This makes it harder to breathe.
Smokers get out of breath when they do exercise.

1 Make a list of the harmful substances in cigarette smoke.

2 Make a list of the parts of the body which are damaged by smoking.

3 Write a few sentences to explain why smokers get more chest infections.

4 Find out what 'passive smoking' is. Write a sentence to explain it.

5 Find out what the word 'addiction' means.

Growing up

As children get older, their bodies grow and change. The things they need and the way they feel often change too.

Children's bodies start to change into adult-like bodies between the ages of nine and seventeen. The time of life when these changes happen is **puberty**. Some of the changes are shown in the pictures below.

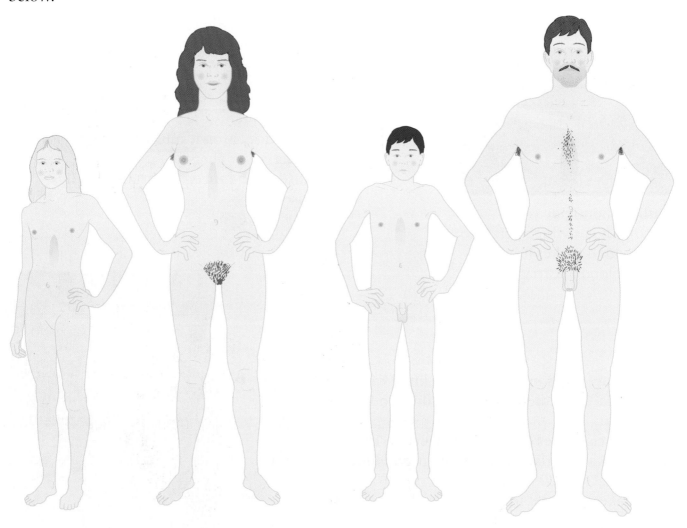

Look at the pictures of how children change into young adults.

1   What do we call the time when our bodies change like this?

2   Write down three ways in which a boy's body changes.

3   Write down three ways in which a girl's body changes.

4   What new things does a young adult need? Write down two things.

5   What does a young adult not need any more? Write down two things.

Sex organs

The **reproductive system** is made of the organs which help to make babies. The organs are different in males and females.

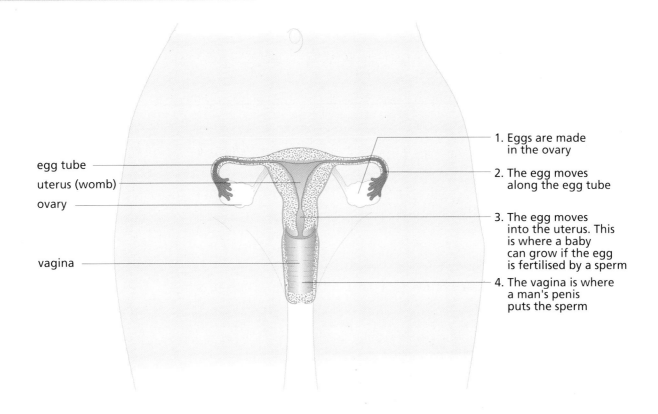

egg tube

uterus (womb)

ovary

vagina

1. Eggs are made in the ovary

2. The egg moves along the egg tube

3. The egg moves into the uterus. This is where a baby can grow if the egg is fertilised by a sperm

4. The vagina is where a man's penis puts the sperm

A woman's **ovaries** make eggs. Each egg contains instructions which will help to make a baby. A new egg is released about every 28 days. The ovaries usually make only one egg at a time. Each egg can grow into a baby.

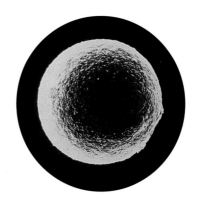

For an egg to grow into a baby, it has to join with a sperm.
Then it needs to stick to the lining of the **uterus**, where it will grow.
If the egg does not join with a sperm, the lining of the uterus is replaced.
This happen about every 28 days.

The old lining of the uterus passes out of the vagina, with a small amount of blood.
This is called 'having a period'. It lasts for several days.
When they are having a period, girls and women may feel tired and have pains.

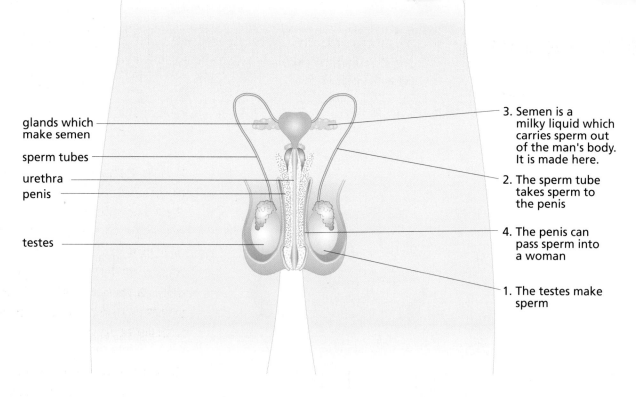

glands which make semen

sperm tubes

urethra
penis

testes

3. Semen is a milky liquid which carries sperm out of the man's body. It is made here.

2. The sperm tube takes sperm to the penis

4. The penis can pass sperm into a woman

1. The testes make sperm

A man's **testes** make sperm. Each sperm contains 'instructions' which will help to make a baby.

Sperm are very small.
They can only be seen using a microscope.
The testes make millions of sperm at a time.
Only one sperm is needed to make a baby.

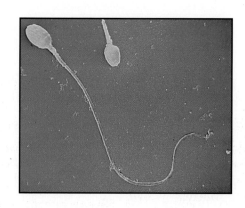

1 Write a list of the parts of the reproductive system in a man.

2 Write a list of the parts of the reproductive system in a woman.

3 Draw a sperm. Which part of the body makes sperm?

4 Draw an egg. Which part of the body makes eggs?

5 Where can a baby grow from an egg?

6 Explain what happens during a 'period'.

Making a baby

To make a baby, a man's sperm has to join with a woman's egg. The decision to make a baby is an important one.

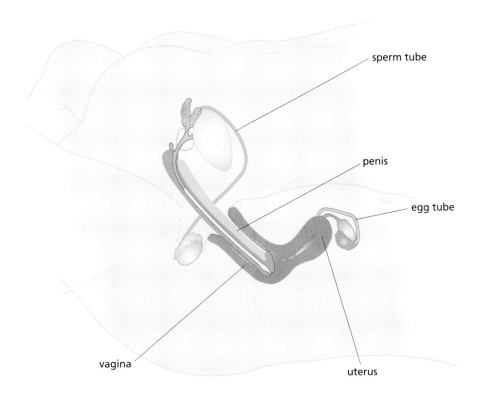

sperm tube

penis

egg tube

vagina

uterus

When a man and woman make love and 'have sex' they become excited. The man's penis become stiff. The woman's vagina becomes wider, and moist. The penis is put inside the vagina. The penis is moved up and down inside the vagina.

When the man becomes very excited he *ejaculates*. Semen is pumped into the vagina. The semen contains millions of sperm. The sperm move up the vagina and into the uterus. They swim into the egg tube. If there is an egg in the tube, the sperm move towards it.

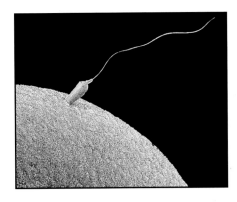

A new life begins when one sperm enters the egg. This is called *fertilisation*.
The egg and sperm have a set of instructions to produce a new individual.
The egg starts to grow into a baby inside the mother's uterus. When the egg starts to grow we say the woman is *pregnant*. She does not release any more eggs while she is pregnant. She does not have periods.

1   List the parts of a man's body which sperm have to pass through.

2   List the parts of a woman's body that sperm have to swim through to find an egg.

3   What happens during fertilisation?

The baby grows inside the mother's uterus.
The baby gets food and oxygen from the
mother's blood. This happens in a special
organ called the **placenta.** The growing baby
is connected to the placenta by its umbilical
cord.
The baby is protected by a bag of liquid.

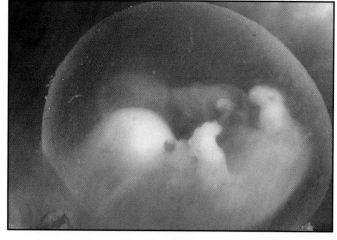

Growing baby at 6–7 weeks

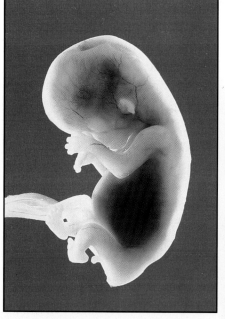

Growing baby at 11 weeks

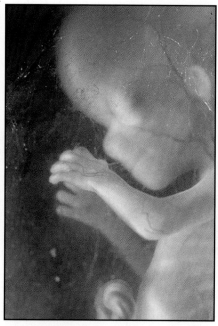

Growing baby at 14–15 weeks

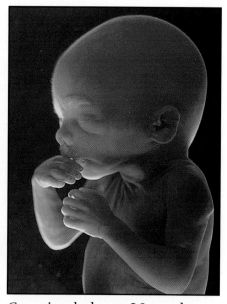

Growing baby at 20 weeks

After 20 weeks, all of the baby's organs have developed.
The baby keeps growing for another twenty weeks.
The mother can feel the baby moving about.
She needs to make sure that she eats a balanced diet.
She must eat enough to get nutrients for herself and the
growing baby.

**Look at the pictures of the developing
baby.**

4   At what age can you first see these parts –

    an eye   an ear   a hand   a leg
    finger nails

5   Write a sentence to explain how the baby
    gets its food and oxygen.

Birth

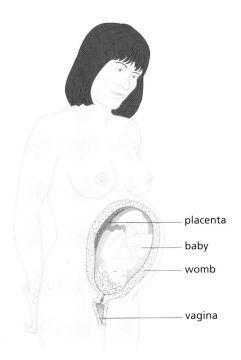

placenta

baby

womb

vagina

This baby is ready to be born.
It is lying head down in the mother's uterus.
This will help it to be born more easily.
The uterus is like a bag made of muscles.
During the birth these muscles push the baby out.

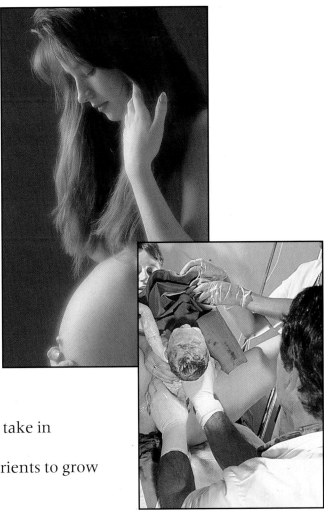

The muscles of the uterus squeeze to push the baby out. The squeeze is called a contraction.
The vagina stretches to let the baby through.
It may take a few hours before the baby is finally born. After the birth the umbilical cord is cut.

The baby is a new individual.
He or she needs to breathe air. The baby's lungs take in oxygen.
He or she needs to be fed to give him or her nutrients to grow and be healthy.
He or she will need a lot of care and attention.

1 How long does a baby grow inside its mother for?

2 What is a contraction?

3 How does the new baby get oxygen?

4 Write a sentence to describe how the baby is pushed out during its birth.

5 Why do you think that babies are usually born head first?

What do forces do?

Lots of things happen because of **forces**.
You can tell there is a force acting when things change.
They may go faster or slower. They may change shape.

Forces can push things. They can pull as well.

You need a force to open a door. A push or a pull will make the door move.

Sometimes a door might stick. It needs a bigger force to move it.

This is because there is a force called friction trying to stop it moving.

If you let go of an egg, it falls down without being pushed. There is a force called **gravity** which pulls it down.

The force of the egg meeting the ground tries to change its shape. But the shell cannot change shape, so it breaks.

Some of the things happening in this picture are caused by forces.

Look carefully to work out what is going on.

1 Write down five changes you can see in the picture.

2 Write down what forces you think are making the changes.

You could start with the egg.

Forces and movement

In short races the start is very important. You need a good push off, so there are special starting blocks. The harder you push on these, the quicker you can increase your speed. This is called **accelerating**.

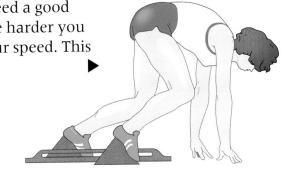

In longer races, it is better to run at a steady speed for most of the race.

Athletes try to save some strength for a burst of acceleration at the end of the race.

A discus thrower needs to spin his body to throw the discus a long way.

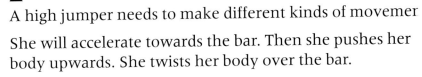

A high jumper needs to make different kinds of movement

She will accelerate towards the bar. Then she pushes her body upwards. She twists her body over the bar.

1   The movement words in the box describe how different athletes move.

Choose the right words for each athlete.

| spin | accelerate | fall |
| twist | slow down | lift |

a) High jumper going over the bar.

b) Discus thrower preparing to throw.

c) Gymnast doing bar exercises.

d) Long jumper on the run to the sandpit.

e) Runner getting tired near the end of the race.

2   For each athlete, write a sentence using the words you have chosen.

Crash protection

When people stop or start quickly, big forces can act on them. These forces can hurt them. They could be hurt in a car crash. Safety devices can protect the body from these forces.

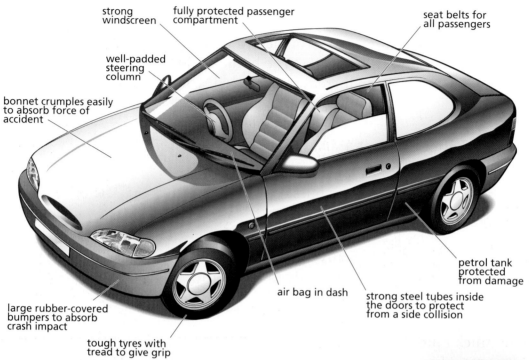

strong windscreen

fully protected passenger compartment

seat belts for all passengers

well-padded steering column

bonnet crumples easily to absorb force of accident

petrol tank protected from damage

air bag in dash

strong steel tubes inside the doors to protect from a side collision

large rubber-covered bumpers to absorb crash impact

tough tyres with tread to give grip

Bumpers at the front and back of a car protect it from being damaged by small bumps. The rubber is bouncy. It absorbs some of the force of the shock.

In a bad accident the forces are much greater. The car will crumple to absorb the shock. This helps to protect the people inside. The strong middle part of the car should not crumple.

Strong seatbelts hold people in their seats. These fabric belts have to stretch a bit so that the people are not injured by the force of a crash.

Babies and small children could easily be hurt in a crash. They need special seats and straps to protect them.

Many new cars also have an air bag. This blows up quickly like a balloon when there is a crash. It acts like a cushion, because it is squashy. It stops the driver from hitting hard parts of the car like the steering wheel.

Cycle safety

People who ride bicycles and motorcycles do not have as much protection as people in cars. They wear hard helmets and other special clothes to help protect them.

1 Write a list of four car safety features. Explain how each one can help.

2 How does a helmet protect a cyclist?

3 Cyclists often wear *reflective* clothing. Find out what 'reflective' means. How does this help to keep them safe?

Friction

When you ride a bicycle, you must learn how to stop safely. You can stop pedalling and slow down. Or you can pull on the brakes, and stop quickly. This is using the force of **friction**. You also need friction to get started.

The picture shows how the brakes work.

The brake lever pulls the blocks. They are squeezed against the wheel. They rub the wheel and the wheel slows down.

This rubbing is called the force of friction. It always tries to stop movement.

If you ride over thick mud there is a lot of friction on the tyres. Mud can be very sticky.

You have to push harder against friction to keep moving.

On the road there is friction because the tyre and the road both have rough surfaces. The tyre grips the road and rolls forward.

If you had completely smooth surfaces there would be no friction. The wheel would keep slipping. It would be impossible to get started.

friction

friction

When it is icy there is almost no friction. Car drivers can put chains on the wheels so they can grip.

Copy out these sentences and fill in the missing words.

1 Brake blocks .... against the wheel to ....the bike.

2 Friction always tries to make things ....

3 It is hard to walk on ice because there is no ....

4 Cars use ....on their wheels in icy weather. This increases ....

Gravity and weight

There is a story that a famous scientist called Isaac Newton got the idea of gravity from watching apples fall off a tree. To remember him we measure forces in newtons. The symbol for newtons is N. The force of gravity on an apple is about 1 newton.

spring force

gravity force

You can measure the force with a force meter.
Hang the apple on a spring which stretches.
Measure the amount of stretch. This is a measure of the force pulling the apple down.

We call this weighing the apple.
The apple has a weight of 1 newton.

The spring pulls up with an equal force. The forces are **balanced** so the apple does not move.

The amount of material in the apple is called the **mass** of the apple.

This is measured in grams.

This apple would have a mass of about 100 grams.

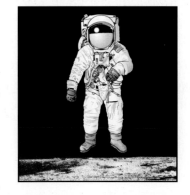

The Moon has less gravity than Earth, so everything weighs less.

If you took the 100 gram apple there it would still be 100 grams in mass. But it would weigh only one sixth of a newton.

Astronauts can jump easily on the Moon, even wearing massive spacesuits. They weigh much less than they do on the Earth. But their mass is still the same.

Copy out these sentences and fill in the missing words.

1   An apple weighs about ....on Earth. The Earth ....the apple. This was discovered by ....

2   Six apples on Earth weigh six newtons.
Their .... is 600 grams.
On the Moon their .... is one newton.
But their mass is still ....

3   Astronauts can jump .... on the Moon than on Earth. There is .... gravity.

Flight

Balloons

When the wind is strong it sometimes feels as if it could lift you into the air.

One way to get air to lift you is with a hot air balloon.

The air inside the balloon is heated by gas burners. The hot air is lighter than cold air so it always rises above the cold air. The hot air inside the balloon rises. It lifts the balloon up.

The balloon will travel whichever way the wind blows it. It comes down to land gently as the air cools.

Parachutes

Another way to float is with a parachute. It traps air underneath the canopy. The air can only get out slowly, so the parachute float down slowly as the person is pulled towards the Earth.

Paragliders are like huge kites which can carry people. The pilot jumps off a high place where there is upward moving air. Strong draughts of upward moving air are called *thermals*. These can make a paraglider rise up for a long way.

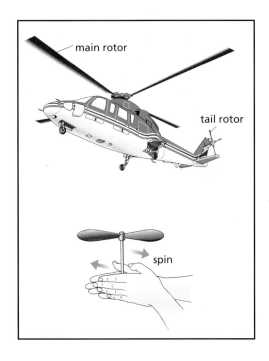

Helicopters

A helicopter has moving blades which push through the air to keep the machine flying. They spin round fast. This makes the air push upwards to support the weight of the helicopter. The upward pushing force of the air is called **lift**.

You can get this effect if you spin a shaped propeller on a stick.

A helicopter can fly in all directions.
It can also stay in one place. This is called hovering.

Aeroplanes

The wings of an aeroplane have a curved upper surface.

The wing shape is called an *aerofoil*. When air moves fast past a wing shape it produces a push upwards.

Aeroplanes have to travel forward fast to get enough lift from the air moving over the wings. That is why they need long runways to pick up speed before they can take off.
They also need large engines to move them forward fast with a big thrust force.

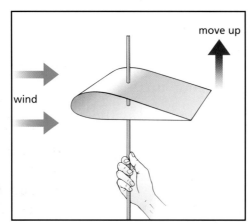

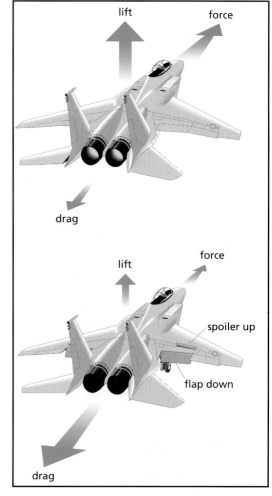

Aeroplanes have a very smooth shape. This reduces the **air resistance**. Air resistance pushes backwards on the plane. This is called the **drag** force. When there is less drag the aeroplane can travel faster.

Before an aeroplane lands it needs to slow down. The shape of the wing is changed by lowering the flaps. The flaps make a bigger drag force.

Copy out these sentences and fill in the missing words.

1 The burners in a hot air balloon heat the air and make it ....

2 To land a balloon safely you need to let it meet the ground ....

3 If a plane is going to crash parachutes can help the people in it because they ....

4 Thermals are made where hot air is moving .... This helps to keep a paraglider ....

5 When an aeroplane is flying, there are four forces acting on it.

These are weight, lift, thrust and drag.

Write a sentence about each.

6 When an aeroplane touches down on the runway you can sometimes see smoke from the tyres. Why does this happen? How do the tyres help to stop the plane? Use the word friction in your answer.

Streamlining

A speedboat has a special shape called a *streamlined* shape. The water is pushed out of the way so that it does not slow down the boat. Streamlining also helps things to travel fast through air.

Air pushes backwards when something tries to move through it quickly. The force is called air *resistance*. You can feel this on a bicycle.

A cyclist can reduce the air resistance by making his or her body shape more smooth and pointed.

Look at the pictures of these two boats.

How can you tell which one is travelling faster?

The speedboat has a powerful engine so it can go faster than the rowing boat. You can see the effect of this in the picture.

The front of the speedboat is called the bow.
The bow is smoothly shaped and comes to a point. It can cut through the water easily. So there is less force from the water pushing the boat backwards.

As water moves quickly past the bow it makes a bow wave. At the back there is a frothy white wake.

Modern cars have smoother shapes than older cars. The streamlined shape lets the air stream, or flow, easily over the body of the car. Their streamlined shape means they can go faster than older cars and use less petrol.

1 Look at the picture of the cyclist. Make a list of the things which make him and the bike streamlined?

2 Cut out or copy pictures of old and modern cars and compare their shapes.

Design a new streamlined car. Draw it and write about its shape.

Combining forces

Forces can be shown with arrows.
The arrows tell you where the force is, and how big it is.
Forces can be added together, or taken away.

20 newtons push

20 newtons gravity

40 newtons push

40 newtons gravity

There are competitions, like the Olympic games, to find the strongest weightlifter. Champions can lift a mass of more than 250 kilograms. That needs a force of more than 2500 newtons to lift it.

In a tug-of-war people use all their *strength* to pull each other over the line.

If the left side pulls harder, the forces will be unbalanced. Everyone will move to the left.

bend   turn   stretch

Dancing and gymnastics can make the body more *supple*.

A supple body can produce forces to bend, stretch and turn more easily.
To stay supple the muscles must be used regularly.

All these exercises use leg and arm muscles to push and pull. Other muscles are used as well. You breathe faster using your chest muscles. The muscles in your heart make it beat faster. This helps to keep your lungs and heart fit and healthy.

Keeping fit makes people strong and supple.

Another kind of fitness is *stamina*. A person with stamina can keep going without getting tired. Some people run a marathon, which is a race of more than 40 kilometres. Each step doesn't take much force, but about 50 000 steps are needed to complete the race!

1 What kind of fitness does a weightlifter need?
2 What kind of fitness does a gymnast need?
3 What kind of fitness does a long-distance runner need?
4 Copy out these sentences. Use the words in the box to fill in the missing words.

> strength   supple   stamina

Riding a bicycle is a good way to keep fit. To ride a long way needs .... The way that the legs have to keep bending will keep them ...... To climb hills and to go fast takes ....

5 Copy out these sentences. Use the words in the box to fill in the missing words.

> balanced   unbalanced

When the tug of war teams hold steady, their forces are ....

When the weightlifter lets the weights drop, the forces are ....

Magnetic forces

Magnets attract some materials and not others,
Magnets attract and **repel** other magnets.
All magnets have a north pole and a south pole.

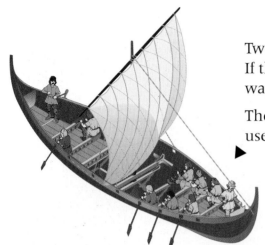

Two thousand years ago the Chinese found a strange stone. If the stone was hung on a string it always pointed the same way. Stones like this always pointed towards the North.

They were natural magnets. For hundreds of years, sailors used these magnetic stones to help steer their ships.

We now use metal magnets called compasses.

One end of the compass points towards North. This end is called the north pole of the compass.

The other end of the compass points towards the South. This end is called the south pole.

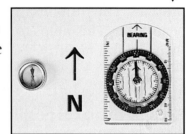

Some materials will stick to magnets. We say they are magnetic.

Some materials will not stick. We say they are non-magnetic.

There are lots of different magnets.

Many magnets are made of steel. Sometimes they are bent into a horseshoe shape.

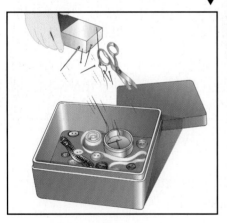

If two magnets are put near to each other the north pole of one will be pulled towards the south pole of the other. We say the poles are attracted.

If you try to put both the north poles of two magnets together they will try to push apart. Two south poles will do the same. We say the poles are repelled.

1　How would you find which direction is North in your school playground?

2　What do we call materials that are attracted to magnets?

3　Two magnets are trying to push each other away. Draw a picture to show where their north poles are.

Using electricity

We use electricity to make machines and electrical equipment work. We use these to make our lives easier and to entertain ourselves.

This picture shows a kitchen in 1901. Very few houses had electricity then.

All the jobs in this kitchen were done without the help of electricity.

Look at the pictures of the two kitchens carefully.

1   a) Which fuel was used to cook food 1901?

   b) Name two different ways in which we use electricity to cook food now.

2   a) How were the clothes washed and dried in 1901?

b) How do we use electricity to wash and dry our clothes now?

3   a) How was the water heated in 1901?

   b) How do you heat the water for washing in your home?

4   Look at the pictures of a modern home. Make a list of ten ways we use electricity at home.

Circuit diagrams

Things that work by electricity have all their parts connected together. They make up an electric **circuit**. The different parts are called the *components* of the circuit.

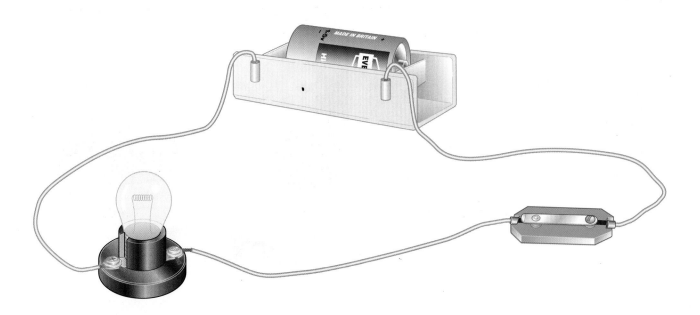

This is a **series circuit**. All the components are connected in a line, one after the other.

This circuit contains a single cell, a lamp and a switch. The components are connected together by wire leads.

It would take a long time to draw a picture of all the components in a circuit. But we can use symbols to show what the components in our circuit are. Many of the symbols look like the component. Some do not, but they are all easy to draw quickly.

Everyone uses the same symbols. So anyone could look at the diagram of the circuit and see how our circuit works and what it is for.

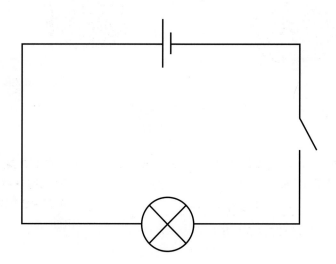

Some of the symbols used in electric circuits –

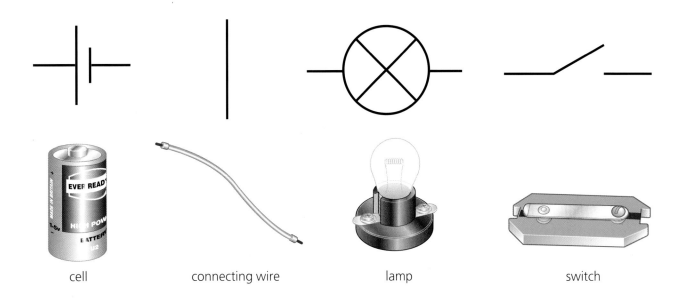

cell   connecting wire   lamp   switch

1 Copy the electrical symbols into your book and label each one.

2 Draw the circuit diagram for the circuit above. Use the correct symbols.

3 Write a sentence to explain why it is better to use a circuit diagram rather than draw a picture for your circuit.

Conductors and insulators

Electrical appliances are connected to the electricity supply by a cable attached to a plug.

The plug fits into a mains electricity socket.

When the plug is switched on an electric current flows through the wires in the cable. The wire **conducts** the electricity to the appliance.

The cable is covered in plastic. This is a material which will not let electricity pass through it. We say it is an insulating material. The outside of the plug is also made of insulating material. Plastic and rubber are both good insulators.

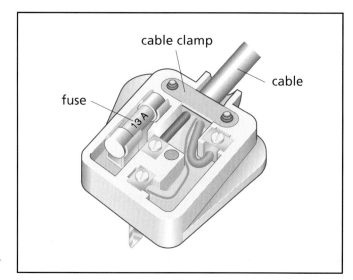

A **fuse** in the plug prevents too much current flowing. The fuse will burn out and break the circuit if the current is too large.

When you push in a plug, the pins of the plug connect with the wires inside the socket. The pins are made of metal which is a good conductor.

You must NEVER put anything in the socket, except a correctly fitted plug.

1 Copy and complete these sentences.

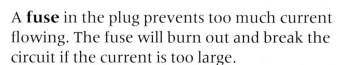

The connecting wires in the cable are made of the metal copper because copper is a good ....

The cable is covered in plastic because plastic is a good ....

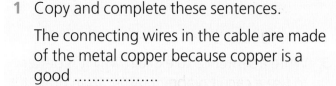

2 Why is it dangerous if electric cables or appliances are not properly insulated?

3 What is a fuse used for?

Controlling the circuit

One of the components used in a circuit is a **resistor**. A resistor makes it more difficult for the current to pass.

A long thin wire has a high resistance. It will not pass as much current as a short fat wire.

A light bulb will shine brighter when there is a bigger current. It can be made brighter or dimmer by changing the resistance in the circuit.

The lighting in a television studio has to be changed all the time.

There are many different lights. Each bank of lights needs a separate circuit to control it.

The resistors in the circuits have sliders. The sliders make the resistance larger or smaller. They are used to make the lights dimmer or brighter.

The lights get dimmer as the resistance increases.

Copy these sentences and fill in the missing words.

1 A light bulb shines brighter when the current is ....

2 A light bulb can be made .... or dimmer by changing the .... in a ....

3 The component that changes the resistance is called a ....

4 The lights get dimmer as the resistance ....

5 A slider can vary the .... of a resistor.

Measuring the current

This circuit uses cells to light the lamp and drive the motor.

When we switch on we say that an electric current flows in the circuit.

We know a current flows because the bulb gets hot and glows and the motor turns.

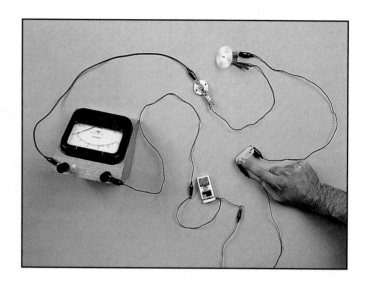

We measure the current in the circuit with an ammeter.

The positive (red) connection must be connected to the positive (+) side of the cell.

The circuit symbol for an ammeter is :

A

Current is measured in amperes. We say amps for short.

The letter A stands for amps.

1 Draw the circuit you would use to measure the current through a lamp. Use the correct circuit symbols.

2 Copy these sentences and fill in the missing words.

We use an .... to measure current.

The unit for measuring current is ....

Electrical forces

There are two kinds of **electric charge**, positive and negative. The forces between electric charges cause thunder and lightning and electric shocks.

The Van de Graaff generator is a machine that can collect electric charge. It contains a rubber belt which can put lots of electric charge on the dome.

If you touch the dome it shares the charge with you. Your body and hair become charged.

Your hair may stand on end because the end of each hair has a positive charge.

When two similar charges meet they repel each other. Each hair tip is pushed away from the next hair.

If you rub two balloons the material of the balloons gets a positive charge.

Because they both have the same kind of charge they repel each other.

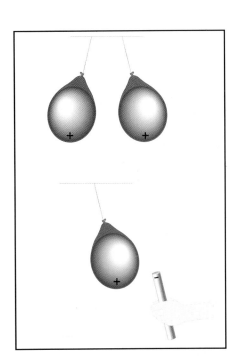

Opposite charges attract each other.

The plastic rod is made of a different material to the balloons.

When you rub the plastic rod it gets a negative charge.

The balloon and the rod are attracted to each other because they have opposite charges.

Copy these sentences and fill in the missing words.

1 There are .... kinds of electric charge.

2 There are .... charges and .... charges.

3 Two charges the same will .... each other.

4 Two different charges will .... each other.

5 The Van de Graaff generator shares its .... with someone touching it. The hair on their head is .... All the hairs .... each other because they have the .... charge.

Electrical safety

Electricity is carried from the power station by power lines. These are big cables held up by high pylons. The cables do not have any insulation around them. There are big insulators on the pylons to stop the electric current passing into the pylons.

The power lines take electricity to lots of electricity substations.
Cables take the electricity from the substations to homes and shops nearby. Most of these cables are underground and they are well insulated.
A substation might supply up to 400 homes.

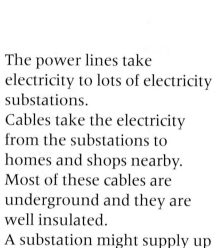

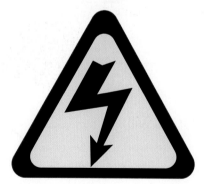

Electricity can catch you by surprise. It can flash through the air, just like lightning. It can kill you without you touching anything.

- Never climb a power pylon.
- Never fly a kite near power lines.
- Never try to get into a substation.

1 What stops the electricity getting from the power lines into the pylons?

2 Write a sentence to explain why you should not fly your kite near power lines.

New substances

Many things we use each day have been made from raw materials from our planet, Earth.
Raw materials can be turned into useful substances by chemical reactions

Many of the substances that we use each day have been made from **raw materials** in the Earth, air or water.

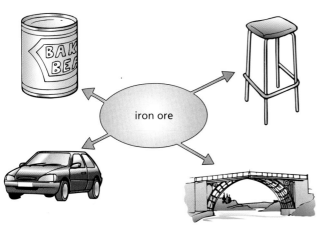

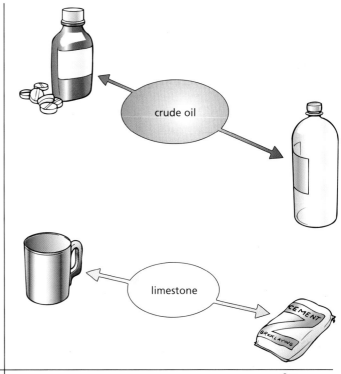

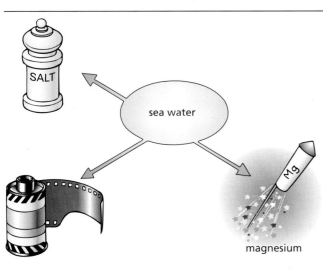

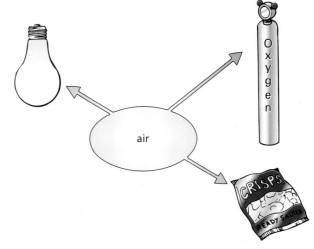

Look at these pictures and then finish these sentences

1 Magnesium and salt are made from ....

2 Iron ore is used to make ....

3 The plastic for a drink bottle is made from ....

4 Argon gas in a light bulb comes from the ....

5 The raw material limestone is used to make ....

Chemical reactions

Only a few materials are used just as they are found.

Some are shown in this camping picture.

The rubber tube on the camping stove is very like the raw material it is made from.

Some materials have to be changed a lot from their raw material.

The metal on the chairs is very different from the metal ore in a rock.

1 Find some materials in the picture that have not changed much from their raw material.

2 Find some materials in the picture that have been changed a lot from their raw material.

3 Which materials have been made using chemical reactions?

Look at the pictures on this page.

Draw a chart like this, and fill it in.

What does the picture show?	Is it a chemical reaction?	Why I think it is, or not

NS3

Lime from limestone

Limestone is dug from the ground. It is turned into lime, by a chemical reaction. Lime is used to make cement.

We use lime to make cement.

We use cement to hold bricks together in a brick wall.

Some buildings are also made from cement.

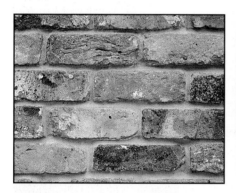

The ancient Greeks and Romans found out how to use lime to make cement.

They also used lime to paint their buildings white.
Lime can be mixed with water to make whitewash.

Many old buildings are still whitewashed.

Farmers and gardeners often add lime to the soil to help plants grow better. The lime makes the soil less acid.

To make lime, limestone or chalk was heated in a lime kiln.

The kiln was heated by burning wood or coal.

The kiln had 'draw holes' at the bottom to let air in. This was also where the wood or coal was added and the lime was taken out.

The farmer would light the kiln when he needed lime – it was his own lime factory!

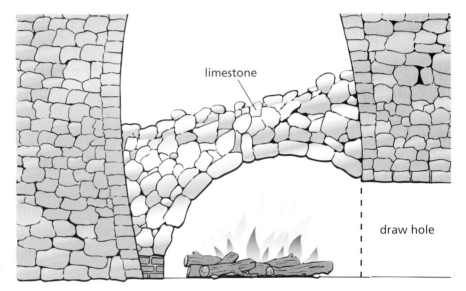

limestone

draw hole

There are many old lime kilns on farms around the country.

This one is in Derbyshire.

1 Give three uses of lime.

2 Why was white a common colour for inside walls in Roman times?

3 What was used to heat the lime?

4 Which picture shows where a chemical reaction takes place?

What in the picture shows you this?

Joseph Priestley

NS4

Joseph Priestley was a famous scientist. He did a lot of experiments. He found out things about gases. He had to design his own apparatus.

Joseph Priestley was born in a village near Leeds in 1733.

Priestley is most famous for his experiments with gases.

He lived near a brewery. He noticed that a lot of gas collected on top of the liquid being made into beer.

He did experiments with this gas. It was carbon dioxide. This is the gas you can make by heating lime.

At that time, gases were usually collected in the bladders of dead animals. Priestley worked out a new way of collecting gases. Over 200 years later we still collect gases in this way.

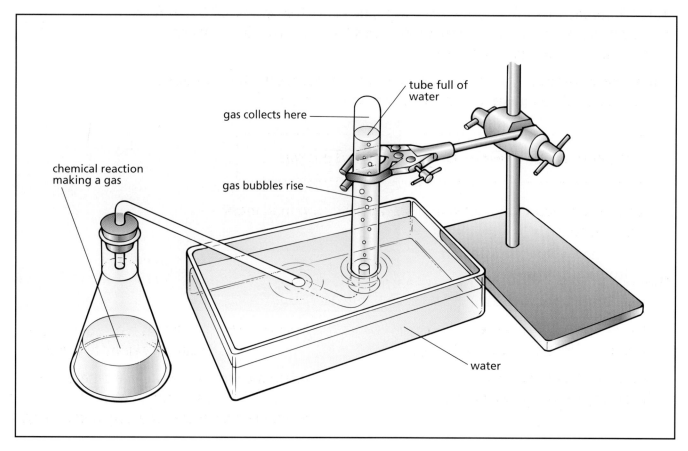

tube full of water

gas collects here

chemical reaction making a gas

gas bubbles rise

water

Priestley wanted to try heating red mercury oxide.

He knew that a candle was not hot enough, so he focused rays from the sun through a big lens on to the container.

We can use a bunsen burner to heat substances. But we do *not* experiment with mercury oxide because it is very poisonous.

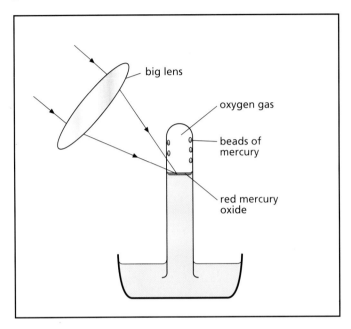

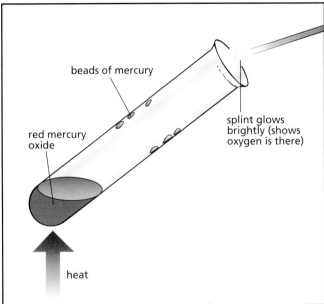

When Priestley heated the mercury oxide, he saw silver-coloured beads form in the container. A gas was formed too. The silver-coloured beads were mercury and the gas was **oxygen**.

When the substance is heated there is a chemical reaction. The substance splits. This is called a **thermal decompostion** reaction

In a chemical reaction the substances change but the total mass stays the same.

Choose the correct word to complete each sentence.

1 Priestley did a lot of work finding out about .... [solids / gases]

2 Priestley collected gases .... [over water / in pigs' bladders].

3 Priestley helped in the discovery of the gas .... [mercury oxide / oxygen].

4 When mercury oxide is heated there .... [is / is not] a chemical reaction which makes mercury and oxygen.

Testing for acids

Acids react with lime scale. We can tell if a liquid is an acid if we measure its **pH.**

Keeping the sink shiny

Chris likes the sink to look shiny. It always looks dull because he lives in an area where the water is 'hard'. The water leaves lime scale in the sink.

He tried using some lime scale remover from the supermarket.

On the bottle it says 'Beware: contains acid'.

The remover reacted with the lime scale. It made a fizzing sound. Chris thought that meant a gas was being made.

When it had finished working, the lime scale was gone.

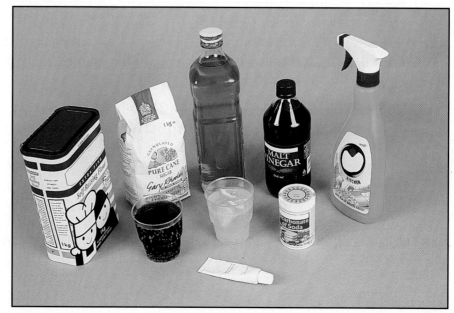

You can find out what other substances at home are acids.

You can find out by testing some of them with **universal indicator** to measure the pH.

Complete these sentences

1 A sink gets dull because of .... in water.

2 We know there was a chemical reaction because Chris heard ....

3 Chris knew a .... was made.

4 An .... gets rid of limescale.

Universal indicator

Universal indicator is used to tell us if a liquid is an **acid** or an **alkali**.

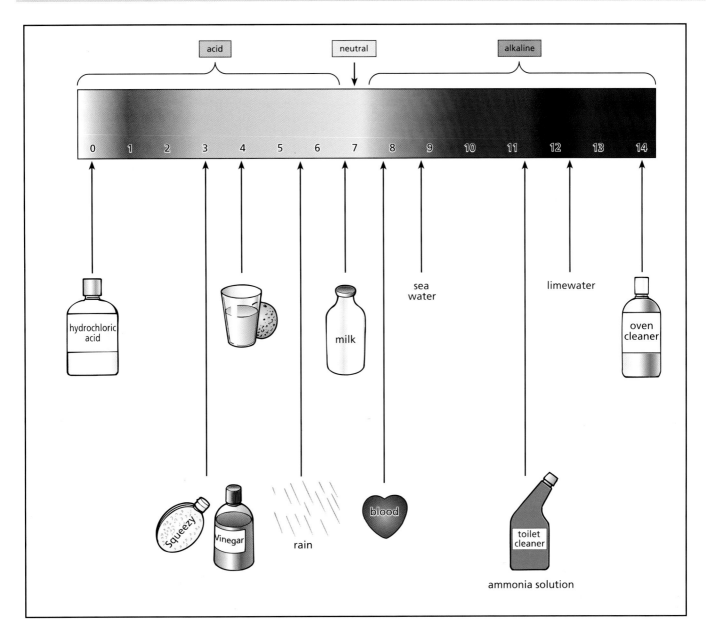

Things that are neither acid nor alkaline are called '**neutral**'.

1 You need to remove limescale from a sink. Will you use an acid, a neutral substance or an alkali?

2 Make a list of all the substances shown in the picture above that you would expect to make the sink shiny.

3 Which substance do you think would work best?

Why do you think it would work best?

Acids and metals

Acids can be used to see if a metal coin is a forgery.

1 We can use acids to see if one of the coins is a forgery.

2 The metals in the coin react with the acid.

3 A spot of the solution is added to the chromatography paper.

4 The paper is stood in solvent.

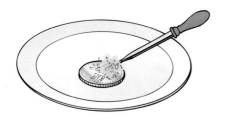

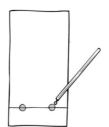

solvent

5 The solvent moves the metals from the coin up the paper.

6 The paper is sprayed and dried. This shows up the metals.

7 The coin on the left is a forgery because it contains an extra metal.

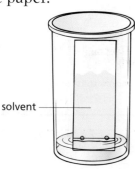

solvent

1 What was used to react with the metals?

2 How do you know there is a chemical reaction in picture 2?

3 Vinegar is a weak acid.

a) Do you think it would react with the coins?

b) Explain why.

4 Why do you think coins are not made of magnesium?

Hydrogen from an acid

Acids react with metals to give a gas.
The gas is **hydrogen**.

Testing for hydrogen

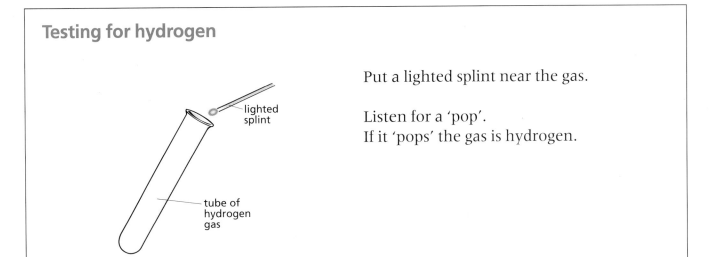

Put a lighted splint near the gas.

Listen for a 'pop'.
If it 'pops' the gas is hydrogen.

lighted splint

tube of hydrogen gas

Testing for carbon dioxide

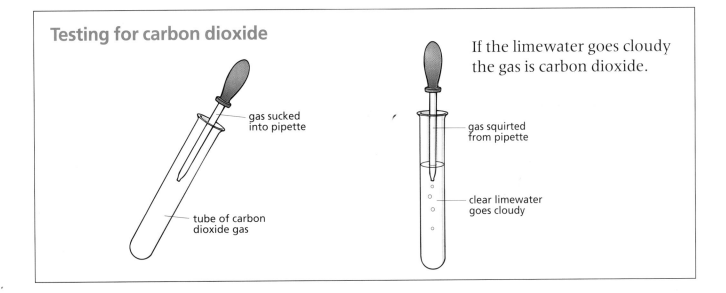

If the limewater goes cloudy
the gas is carbon dioxide.

gas sucked into pipette

gas squirted from pipette

tube of carbon dioxide gas

clear limewater goes cloudy

The fizzing that we see when we add acid to a
metal is hydrogen gas.

1   Draw a diagram to remind you how to test
    for

    a) hydrogen

    b) carbon dioxide

2   Which of these two gases can we get from
    a metal when we add acid?

Burning

Burning is not the same as heating. You can warm bread and it is still the same, but if you burn the pitta bread it will look very different.

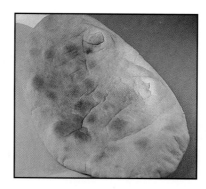 

When you burn a substance you get different products. Burning is a very important chemical reaction.
When something burns it gives off energy. We feel this as 'heat'.

When a substance burns it reacts with the air.

Air is a mixture of gases. When a substance burns it reacts with the oxygen in the air. We say oxygen is a **reactant** in burning.

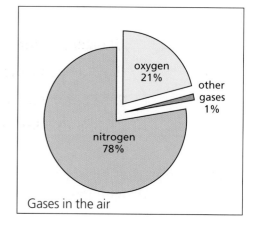

Gases in the air

1 Which of these is an example of a chemical reaction?

  • warming bread

  • making toast

  How do you know this?

2 What gas in the air is needed for burning?

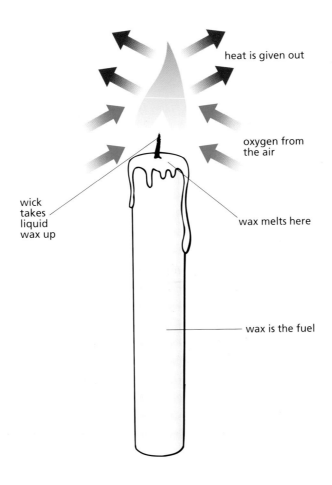

heat is given out

oxygen from the air

wick takes liquid wax up

wax melts here

wax is the fuel

A substance that burns is called a **fuel**.

The fuel in a candle is wax.

The wax reacts with oxygen from the air.

Carbon dioxide and water are made in this reaction.

We also feel the 'heat' energy that is made.

1   What happens when you light the wick?

2   Why does the wax melt?

3   Will the candle stay alight in a place with no air?

4   Imagine your best friend does not understand how a candle works. Write what you would say to him or her to explain it

Smoke

When fuels burn in air they make smoke.
This can be bad for your health.

Burning fuels often make smoke. Smoke comes from homes, factories and cars. Smoke contains small particles of carbon and tar. Smoke is bad for people's health.

The carbon settles on buildings and plant leaves and makes them black. The tar contains some substances that might cause cancer.

If there is a lot of smoke in the air sunlight cannot get through. Then plants cannot grow so well.

In London in 1952 it was very foggy. Smoke mixed with the fog to form *smog*. The smog hung over London for five days.

People could not stop their eyes from watering and they coughed a lot. Many old and sick people could not breathe properly. Lots of people became very ill, hospitals had no spare beds and over 4000 people died.

Now there are Clean Air Acts which mean that coal cannot be burned in London and other big cities. Today, London is a much cleaner place. Over 50 more species of birds can now be seen in London. It is now much sunnier in London than it used to be.

However, people in London have to burn more expensive smokeless fuel if they want to have an open fire.

Smoke

1 How is smoke made?

2 Why is smoke harmful?

3 Why is smoke particularly dangerous on a day when it is not windy?

4 How have the Clean Air Acts improved London?

5 Clean air may still be dangerous to health. Why is this?

Putting out fires

To put out a fire we must take away the fuel, or the oxygen (in the air) or the heat. We only need to take one of these away.

In 1666, in the Great Fire of London, 13 200 homes were destroyed. The buildings were mostly made of wood and were close together. There were no water pipes, so the water had to be carried on carts. The fire burned for many days.

Three things are needed for a fire: fuel, heat and oxygen. We can put these together into a *fire triangle*.

To put out a fire you have to take away one of these three things.

Look at these pictures. Write down which part of the fire triangle is being taken away in each picture?

Fuels for the body

As you read this book there are chemical reactions happening in your cells. Fuels are burning to give you enough energy to read this. Oxygen from the air you breathe is needed to make the fuels burn.

Marshmallows and bread are two fuels your body can burn. We can burn them in an experiment to see how much energy we can get from them.

This is the food taken from a pupil's lunch box. You can see how much energy each type of food will give to your body.

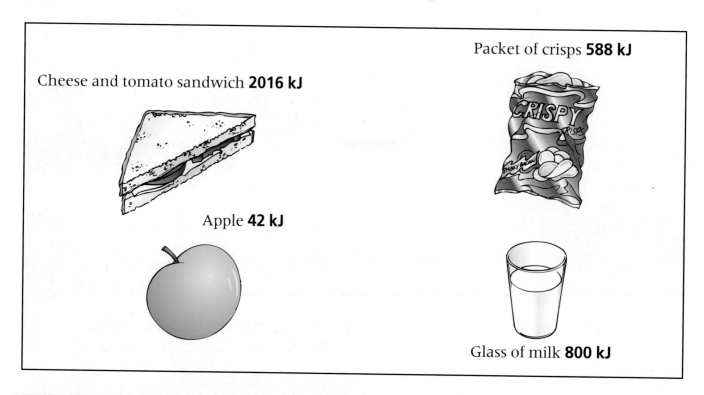

Packet of crisps **588 kJ**

Cheese and tomato sandwich **2016 kJ**

Apple **42 kJ**

Glass of milk **800 kJ**

Use these words to finish the following sentences:

| oxygen | burns | energy |

1   In the body there is a chemical reaction when food ....

2   In this chemical reaction .... is given out.

3   Food reacts with .... when it burns.

4   List the foods from the lunch box in order. Start with the one that will give the body most energy.
    Finish with the one that will give the body least energy.

Burning fuels

Fuels are burnt with oxygen to give energy.

Burning is a chemical reaction. One of the **reactants** is a **fuel**.
The other reactant is **oxygen**. When the fuel burns the products are called oxides. Burning coal produces carbon dioxide and water. We usually burn fuels to get the energy from them. We can feel this as 'heat', and we might see flames as well.

> **Fuel + oxygen** gives **oxides**

A good fuel produces a lot of energy

You might see the word **combustion.**
This means the same as burning.

Look at the picture and find all the different fuels that are being used. Work out what each fuel is being used for.

Record your answers in a table like this.
(The first one has been done for you.)

Fuel	What it is being used for
Food	To give people energy.

Controlling burning

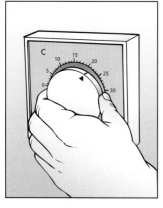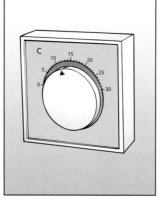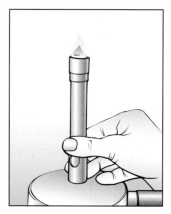

1 a thermostat

2 a bunsen burner

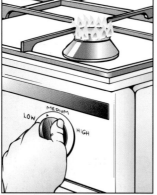

3 a gas cooker

4 a wood-burning stove

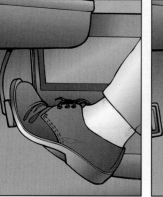

5 a car engine

6 a person

Controlling burning

For each pair of pictures write a sentence to describe how the burning is being controlled.

One is done for you:

Turning down the thermostat reduces the flow of fuel to the central heating boiler so less fuel burns.

Pollution

Sulphur dioxide is a waste gas. It is made when oil and coal burn.

We burn a lot of fuels in this country. We need to burn fuels at home, to keep us warm in winter and to cook our food.

Every time you use electricity, a fuel is being burned. You cannot see this happening, but fuels are being burned at power stations to make the electricity.

Many power stations burn coal or oil. These fossil fuels contain a lot of sulphur. When the suphur reacts with oxygen it forms sulphur dioxide. Some of this is collected, but a lot escapes up the chimney.

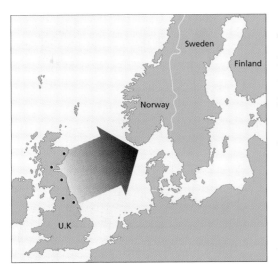

The sulphur dioxide reacts with rain. It is one of the substances in 'acid rain'. This affects plants.

The wind blows the air over to Sweden and it is thought that the acid rain affects the trees like this.

Acid rain

Look at the map above.

People in Sweden think that their trees are being damaged by acid rain caused by power stations in the United Kingdom.

1 Why do you think Sweden might be correct?

The Government in this country says that Sweden cannot be sure that the acid rain is coming from the United Kingdom.

2 Why do you think the Government might be correct?

The bunsen burner

When a fuel burns it gives out energy.

We see this energy as light. We feel it as heat.

When a fuel burns, carbon dioxide and water are produced.

The gas used for a bunsen burner is a fuel. The name of this fuel is methane.

How a bunsen burner works

We use bunsen burners to make chemical reactions happen.

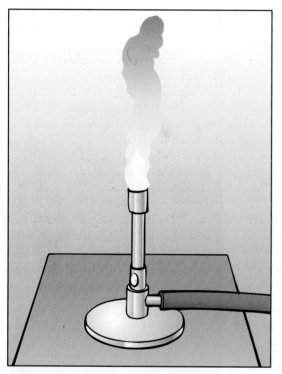

Yellow flame – safety flame

Blue flame – used for heating

When the air hole is closed it keeps out some air. The gas burns quietly with a yellow flame. The yellow flame is less hot. It is the safety flame.

When the air hole is open a lot of air is used. This makes the flame fierce, blue and hot. The blue flame is the heating flame.

1 Which coloured flame is the safest?

2 Which coloured flame is the hottest?

3 How do you alter your bunsen burner to make it heat something quickly?

4 Should the hole be open or closed before you light a bunsen burner?

Glossary

Absorb   This means to soak up.

Accelerate   This means to speed up and go faster.

Acid   This is a substance that gives pH 0–6 when we use universal indicator. The paper goes red or orange.

Adaptation   Something which helps a living thing to fit into its environment. For example the shape of a bird's beak, so it can eat special food.

Air resistance   This is the force of the air against something moving. It makes the thing move more slowly.

Alkali (or alkaline)   This is a substance that gives pH 8–14 when we use universal indicator. The paper goes blue-green to dark blue. An alkali is the 'opposite' to an acid.

Anther   The part of a flower which makes pollen.

Antiseptic   This is a chemical substance that helps stop bacteria growing.

Bacteria   These are very small living things. Some cause diseases, like food poisoning. Others are useful to us.

Balance   Something that is balanced has equal forces acting on it on each side. It stays steady.

Boiling   This can happen when a liquid is heated. Lots of big bubbles come to the surface of a liquid and burst. A pure liquid boils at a steady temperature.

Burning   This is a chemical reaction. A substance reacts with oxygen and we also feel 'heat' from the reaction.

Carbohydrates   These are substances in our food which give us energy.

Carbon dioxide   This is a gas. If we add carbon dioxide to clear limewater, the limewater goes cloudy. Carbon dioxide is formed in a burning reaction.

Carpel   The part of a flower which contains the ovule.

Chemical reaction   There is a chemical reaction if we make a new different substance. We can also look to see if light or 'heat' are given out.

Chromatography   This is the way of separating different colours that are dissolved in a liquid.

Circuit   This is the complete path from a cell through a lamp or other components and back to the cell.

Circulatory system   This is the parts of the body which move blood around. It includes the heart, arteries and veins.

Classify   This means to put things into groups which are the same in some way.

Combustion   This is another word for burning.

Condensation   This is what happens when a gas turns back to a liquid.

Conductor   This is a material which will allow a current of electricity to flow through it.

Constellation   A pattern of stars seen in the sky at night.

Contracts   When a muscle gets shorter it contracts.

Decibel   This is the unit for measuring how loud a sound is (dB).

Decomposer   A living thing which feeds on dead things and makes them rot away.

Diaphragm   (di-a-fram) This large muscle helps us to breathe.

Diffusion   This happens when particles of gas spread out. They move around until they are all spread out evenly. Liquids can also diffuse.

Digestive system   The parts of the body which help us to digest food make up the digestive system. It includes the stomach and intestines.

Disinfectant   This is a chemical that kills germs.

Dissolve   When a solute mixes in with a liquid to form a solution we say the solute dissolves. When a substance dissolves the solution that forms will look transparent.

Distillation   This is the way to get a liquid back from a solution. First the liquid is made to evaporate, then it condenses.

Drag   This is a force caused by air resistance or water resistance. It slows down something that is moving.

Electric charge   Something that contains an electric force is charged. It can be a positive charge or a negative charge.

Electric current   This is a flow of electricity. Electric current transfers energy to make things work.

Evaporation   This happens when a liquid turns into a gas.

Excrete   This means to get rid of waste made in the body.

Fertilisation   This is what happens when pollen and an ovule, or sperm and an egg, join to make a new individual.

Filter   This is one way to separate a solid from a liquid.

Filtrate   This is the liquid that goes through the filter paper.

Force   A force is a push or pull that changes the movement or the shape of things. Force is measured in newtons.

Freezing   This happens when a liquid turns to a solid.

Friction   This is a force which affects the way things move. Friction slows things down.

Fuel   This is a substance that reacts with oxygen in a burning reaction. When paper burns, the paper is called a fuel.

Fungi   A group of living things which includes mushrooms and toadstools.

Fuse   A thin piece of wire in a circuit. If the wires in the circuit get too hot the fuse melts and breaks the circuit.

Gas   In a gas the particles are far apart and they move very fast. Oxygen is a gas.

Germination   This is what happens when a young plant starts to grow from a seed.

Gravity   This is a force caused by the Earth. It pulls things downwards. It is measured in newtons.

Habitat   The place where an animal or plant lives.

Hydrogen   This is a gas. If we put a lighted splint with hydrogen we get a loud 'pop'. Hydrogen is the gas that we see as the 'fizz' when an acid is added to a metal.

Image   This is what we see in a mirror.

Incubator   This is a machine which helps to keep babies warm.

Insoluble   When a solid does not dissolve in a solvent it is called insoluble.

Insulator   This is a material which will not allow electricity to flow through it.

Lift   This is the force which holds up aeroplanes when they are flying.

Light ray   A very thin beam of light.

Liquid   In a liquid the particles are all touching but moving about. A liquid takes the shape of its container. Water is a liquid.

Loudness   This is how loud or quiet a sound is.

Luminous   Something which makes light and sends it out as light rays is luminous.

Magnitude scale   This is how we measure how bright a star is.

Mass   This is how much stuff there is in something. Mass is measured in grams or kilograms.

Material   This is the stuff that a thing is made from. A ball is made from the material called rubber.

Melting   This happens when a solid turns to a liquid.

Micro-organisms   These are very small living things which can only be seen using a microscope.

Mixture   A mixture contains at least two different substances. The substances may be gases, liquids or solids.

Neutral   This is a substance that gives pH 7 when we use universal indicator. The paper goes green. This substance is between an acid and an alkali on the pH scale.

Non-luminous   Something which does not make light is non-luminous.

Nutrients   These are substances in food which living things need to keep them alive and healthy.

Opaque   Something opaque does not let light pass through. You cannot see through an opaque object.

Orbit   This means to go round. The Earth orbits the Sun. The path of the Moon moving around the Earth, or of a planet moving around the Sun is called its orbit.

Ovaries   These are the parts of the female body which make eggs.

Ovule   The female part of a flower which makes a seed.

Oxygen   This gas is used in many chemical reactions. It is needed for a substance to burn.

pH   This is a scale that tells us if a substance is acid, neutral or alkali. It also tells us how acid or alkali the substance is.

Photosynthesis   This is the name for the way green plants make sugar, using light for energy.

Pitch   This is used to describe how high or low a sound is.

Placenta   This is the part of a woman's body which provides a growing baby with food and oxygen from its mother's blood.

Pollen   The male part of a flower which makes a seed.

Predator   An animal which hunts and kills other animals for food.

Predict   This means to know in advance. We try to predict the result of an investigation.

Prey   An animal which is eaten by another animal.

Product   This is a substance that is made in a chemical reaction. For example carbon dioxide is made in burning, so carbon dioxide is a product.

Property   The properties of a material tell you what the material is like. For example, a metal is hard and shiny.

Proteins   These are substances in food which we need to help us to grow.

Puberty   This is the time of life when a child's body start to change into an adult body.

Pure substance   This is a single substance that has a definite melting and boiling point. It has a chemical symbol or formula.

Raw material   This is material that we use just as we find it. The material might come from the ground or a plant or animal. Wood is a raw material.

Reactant   This is a substance that takes part in a chemical reaction. For example oxygen is needed for burning, so oxygen is a reactant.

Reflection   Light is reflected when it hits an object. The reflected light bounces back. You see reflection in a mirror.

Repel   This means push away. Similar poles of magnets repel each other.

Reproduce   This means to make new individuals, or produce young.

Reproductive system   The parts of a woman's or man's body which can help to make a new individual are called the reproductive system.

Residue   This is the solid left on the filter paper.

Resistor   This is a material which does not allow electricity to flow very easily

Respiration   This is the way living things get their energy from food.

Respiratory system   The parts of the body which help to take in oxygen and to get rid of carbon dioxide make up the respiratory system.

Series circuit   This is an electric circuit in which all the components are in line and the electric current flows through them all.

Shadow   This is the dark area behind an opaque object, where there is less light.

Solid   In a solid, the particles are touching and only moving a little by vibrating 'on the spot'. Ice is a solid.

Solubility   If a solute dissolves easily in a liquid the solute has a high solubility. We say the solute is very **soluble**.

Solute   This is the solid that you use when you make a solution.

Solution   This is made when a solute mixes in with a solvent. Solutions are transparent.

Solvent   This is the liquid that you use when you make a solution

Source   The place or thing something comes from.

Species   A group of living things which can reproduce with each other.

State (of a substance)   This is a solid, liquid or gas.

Stigma   The part of a flower which collects pollen.

Suspension   When a liquid contains insoluble material we call it a suspension.

Testes   These are the parts of a male body which make sperm.

Thermal decomposition   This is a chemical reaction that needs heat (thermal). The substance that you start with is split (decomposition). When we heat limestone it splits to make two different substances.

Thrust   This is the force of the engine which makes things move.

Translucent   Something translucent lets light pass through but scatters it. You cannot see clearly through a translucent object.

Transparent   Something transparent lets light pass through. You can see through a transparent object.

Universal indicator   We use this to tell us if a substance is an acid, alkali or neutral. It is a liquid or paper which changes colour.

Uterus   This is the part of a female where a baby grows. It is also called the womb.

Vacuum   This is a space with nothing in it, not even air.

Vapour   This is a cloud of liquid particles. Steam is water vapour.

Variation   The differences between living things.

Vertebrate   A group of animals which have skeletons inside their bodies, with a backbone.

Vibration   This is a to-and-fro movement. Vibrating objects make sound.

Vitamins   These are substances in our food which we need, in small amounts, to keep us healthy.

Wave   This is made by vibrations going through something. Sound waves are vibrations in air.